Praise for

LIVING AND DYING WITHOUT A MAP

"We know it is a fact that we all die, but it is so hard to truly believe it will happen to us. I had the privilege of caring for Greg Ewert and his family during treatment for his brain tumor. Over the years since, I have shared their story of community, love, and the embracing of a life well lived. If there is such a thing as a 'blueprint for a good death,' this is it."

Lynne P. Taylor, MD, FAAN
Alexander M. Spence–Endowed Chair in Neuro-Oncology
Clinical Professor
Codirector, Alvord Brain Tumor Center
Departments of Neurology, Neurologic Surgery, and Seattle Cancer
Care Alliance, UW Medicine

"'My wish for all is to be speakers of our truths,' Greg Ewert once wrote. He and his wife speak with clarity and eloquence their own hard truths about loss, love, and healing in the face of death. This is a story for anyone who has said, 'I don't know how you do it,' or who may be asked to take this tumultuous, confusing journey 'without a map.' Theirs is a story written on our hearts."

Elizabeth Landrum, PhD
Clinical Psychologist
Specializing in life-limiting illness, grief, and loss

"A terrible yet beautiful book, documenting one family's passage through the gifts and tragedies of terminal disease, Nancy Ewert's honest and illustrative account of her husband's battle with brain cancer serves as a guide for others to help their loved ones die well by living even better. She shows us how hope springs eternal, yet is transformed through the process: first for cure, then for good days, then for peace. To read this book, you will be as inspired by a wonderful man and his steadfastly supportive friends and family as you [are] shown a path through the unknowingness of disease process."

Bob Laws
Hospice RN

3/30/20

Dear Elly,

As we travel through life's complicated terrain, may we know we are never really alone ~

LIVING AND DYING
WITHOUT A MAP

With love and blessings,

Nancy
Ebert

LIVING AND DYING WITHOUT A MAP

ONE FAMILY'S JOURNEY THROUGH THE WORLD OF GLIOBLASTOMA

Nancy Ewert

MOUNTAIN ARBOR
PRESS
Alpharetta, GA

The author has tried to recreate events, locations, and conversations from her memories of them. The author has made every effort to give credit to the source of any images, quotes, or other material contained within and obtain permissions when feasible.

ISBN: 978-1-63183-627-5 - Paperback
eISBN: 978-1-63183-628-2 - ePub
eISBN: 978-1-63183-629-9 - mobi

Printed in the United States of America   0 2 1 7 2 0

♾This paper meets the requirements of ANSI/NISO Z39.48-1992 (Permanence of Paper)

"the end" by Andrew Michael Roberts is used by permission of the author, from *Something Has to Happen Next*, University of Iowa Press, 2009.

"Pacific" by Jessica Gigot is an excerpt from the longer poem "Making Ceremony by the Sea," used by permission of the author, from *Flood Patterns*, Antrim House, 2015.

To my children, Emma, Lilly, and Clara, and to Greg's devoted siblings, Mary, Jane, and Dave, and their children, Jessica, Erika, Sarah, and Chris

Grief is praise, because it is the natural way love honors what it misses.

—Martín Prechtel, "The Smell of Rain on Dust"

CONTENTS

INTRODUCTION

I don't understand so many things.
Still, we must tell what we know.

—Naomi Shihab Nye, "Member of the Tribe"

One word can change a life
The lips of the ER doctor formed a word
The word opened a crack
Into it we fell
An unknown world
One word can change a life

For some, it is a phone call, and for some, a knock on the door. For me, it was a single word: *glioblastoma*. With this word, our family was thrust into a world that we did not choose to live in, nor would we ever wish to visit.

Overnight, we were inhabitants of that world. There were no maps. At times the path was clear, and at times it was obscured. This journal is the story of how we found our way.

Some signposts bore terrifying words: chemotherapy, average length of time, radiation, medication list, seizures, and eventually, walker, wheelchair. Then came hospice, bath aid, hospital bed, catheter, morphine, and the last word, death.

But, there were other signs that became illuminated and illuminating: words like family, love, cooked and delivered meals, friendship, washed laundry, laughter, memories, bearing witness, four o'clock chore guys, daughters, singing, gathering around, hummingbirds, night guys . . . gratitude.

This book is made entirely of writings by my husband, Greg, myself, and our children during the time of his illness. My voice and our daughters' voices are in plain text, and Greg's voice is in italics. The writing reflects the unfolding of understanding and events as a dialogue on the CaringBridge website, with added entries from my personal journals. "Nancy's Journal" entries are direct quotes from my personal journals—a lifeline for me. Although these journal entries were not originally intended for publication, I am sharing them now in hopes that they add a level of honesty to the story. I have chosen to leave the typos and funny misspellings in Greg's entries, because they show how his capacities and awareness were changing over time—as well as his beautiful heart, always.

The book is addressed to you, and that "you" is the varied readers of our CaringBridge.org website, which were made up of our neighbors on our island off the coast of Washington State, the community around the school where Greg worked, our families, and the many loving friends from near and far who joined us as we walked this road. Now, that "you" includes the person reading right now, and I invite you to our side.

This book is my way of sharing gratitude, hope, and acceptance. I hope it may shine light upon the paths of others.

CHAPTER 1

AUGUST 2010

Let the pain be pain,
not in the hope that it will vanish
but in the faith that it will fit in,
find its place in the shape of things

—Albert Huffstickler, "The Cure"

August 21

NANCY'S JOURNAL

Oh God, Greg has a brain tumor. How can I even write these words? So many words I have wanted to write in the last two days. I feel like I have lived a lifetime in the last 48 hours. August 18, my 60th birthday – laughing, drinking tequila, singing, acting silly and having so much fun with those I love and here I am, barely three days later, with Emma on the floor crying herself to sleep and all of us facing a future of illness and maybe the untimely death of Greg, whom I love with all of my heart and soul. How can this be?

It is like we have been transported by some futuristic vehicle into another land. Life is just the same, but all of a sudden, a totally different color. Nothing will ever be the same – nothing ever again. There is no future.

Greg cries – all he wanted was to be able to see his grandchildren grow up. All of our dreams – marrying daughters, becoming grandparents, will they be gone?

As I write and try to reflect on these two days, it is a blur. So many little stupid things have happened that we have even laughed about but then the big black wall slams down again. I see people in the hospital and feel badly for one person or another, and then I realize that our situation may be worse than anyone else's.

August 22

NANCY'S JOURNAL

I wake up to a living nightmare. I can only get to sleep with a sleeping pill, and then it is only for seven hours and I wake up jittery and sad. I want to be with Greg and feel the warmth of his body – alive – but he is in a cold hospital bed across the city. In two hours, we will hear the verdict from the MRI. Is this what people in court on trial feel like when the jury comes out?

Emma and Clara are here, and we are all one huge ball of sadness, grief, and fear, and love. Emma has to leave tomorrow night. How can she do it? I know she asks herself that now – but I also think she should go back to school.

On a deep level, I expect the worst: that Greg will die from this. And yet maybe I am just doing that in my mind and it won't be true. Maybe I am just being negative. If I heard one ounce of hope from this meeting today, I would not feel this way. I have just never seen anyone make it through this alive. I know Greg sees this too. My brain is crazy now. I have a thought and can't remember it two seconds later. I feel like I have so much responsibility with the girls here and that they really need me (of course they do) and I can't really need, too. It is all so so B-I-G, SO BIG and VERY VERY SCARY.

August 22

NANCY'S JOURNAL

We came home today. Now Emma and I are snuggling and watching a movie. Overwhelmed. I am so tired of talking on the phone, and then I feel badly for that. I hate it when people stop by without calling, but I hate it when people call.

August 24

NANCY'S CARINGBRIDGE LETTER

Greg has been diagnosed with a brain tumor. It is shocking, terrifying and sad for all of us.

On the day after my 60th birthday, our family of five took a trip to Mt. Rainier to celebrate. We had an enjoyable night together, but it became evident that we needed to go to the ER as Greg's speech was compromised and his left foot was dragging.

We still do not have all the information that we desperately want. He has had a CT scan and an MRI, and there is an obvious abnormality that they can tell is a malignant tumor. The neurosurgeon's best guess is NOT a good scenario, but he stressed that until he does the surgery, he will not know for sure. Surgery is scheduled for August 31st. As much of the tumor as possible will be removed and sent to pathology. Then we must wait another week for the conclusive results. At that time, we will most likely be going down the oncology route, which will consist of oral chemo and radiation.

As you can imagine, the girls are absorbing this news with difficulty. Emma leaves tonight for the airport to go back to McGill University. It is hard for her but the right thing for now. Lilly starts school on September 20th in Oregon, so she will still be here when Greg has his surgery. And of course, Clara is here for the duration.

We are all grateful to have been together these few days as we each try to absorb this huge blow. In addition to the tears we have shared, we have had some good laughs together, too. For this week, we want to be here, be normal and be together without a lot of engagement with the outside world. It feels good to cook and just be normal.

All your messages, hugs, love, support and prayers are incredibly helpful and nourish us in ways we never imagined. We are grateful. We hope you will understand the energy each conversation requires and that we need to balance that energy for ourselves as well.

August 26

GREG'S CARINGBRIDGE LETTER

Only one week ago our family vacation was rudely interrupted by a trip to the urgent care faciility because I was having difficulty forming my words – not like me! Two CAT scans later, the doctor told our family the news that I have a tumor and she is sending me to Viriginia Mason Hospital for an MRI and further treatment. The news ripped through us in a way I have never experienced before. We held each other sobbing and wishing that my greatest fear of a small stroke would return.

Now, one week later, I am sitting on our couch, a quiet morning at 3:00 trying to type "My Story". My life has been turned upside down and it is filled with bittersweet ironies that occur every day around the world. I have to make this short and to the point because the tumor has robbed of my ability to use a key board – my left hand's coordination is compromised and typing is vey difficult. (Thank God I have Nancy for communication!)

I want to tell people how much I appreciate the outpouring of love and support. I have felt bathed in love. I have had visions of what would happen in our busy world if we would all stop and tell those people that have touched our lives how much we care for them. Thank you for your honest, reflective thoughts.

The paradox is this has been one of the mot wonderful weeks of my life – from deep conversations to talking with people I see rarely to beating my ping-pong buddy 2 out of 3 (thank goodness my right is still okay!) outdoors on a sunny afternoon with close friends near by to gathering at 6:30 am four mornings in a row with two of my best men friends for coffee, bullshit and a reality check. The week ending last night at the Bay Cafe for our 22nd wedding aniversary – looking into the eyes of my beautiful wife watching the sun set over the water realizing my greatest gift in my life was a chance boat trip to the San Juan Islands 42 years ago which eventually landed me on our sweet island filled with love.'

So this time period shifts Tuesday with my surgery and the next phase of the battle. I want you to know I am headed into the battle *carrying your love an support, seeking the light, the spirit of the grizzly bear on my back – miracles abound and I do believe in miracles and the mystery of life.*

I have given myself permission to say whatever I want to this week – a sweet freedom so I end with a request to tell some people this week how much you love them – take TIME to do what is importantant.

August 26

NANCY'S CARINGBRIDGE LETTER

Early morning thoughts: I walk around the house feeling filled with gratitude. All your love and offers of support, food, housing, dog care, the prayer flags, the emails, the calls, the notes in my mailbox, the gifts, the information… I wish my brain were a computer so I could keep it all there safely on my hard drive and access it over and over. Each gesture is written on my heart and I will re-visit each one through the rest of my days. We have taken in each comment and expression and are holding you all quite close.

I find it hard to believe that one week ago we were celebrating my birthday and being silly and fun. We have lived an eternity in this past week. I hope I can find an adequate way to express how much it helps to have so many people care so much. Greg's heart has never been fuller. Maybe this time he will get it what a wonderful person he is in this world? He is understanding how much he is loved. We are both humbled and amazed. What a remarkable man Greg is – he keeps on giving even now.

Thank you again for grieving with us, holding us up, and loving us. Your reaching out feels good to us. We want to interact, and sometimes, we just have to stop for a while and gather in with each other.

I have never really understood the word "paradox" as much as I do now. I need all of you so much and I need to be alone and quiet to absorb it all. I want to laugh and I need to cry. My children need me more than ever and I need them and I desperately want to be alone sometimes. I know anyone would help me and I still need to sort through my desk and organize details that no one else can do. There are much bigger paradoxes that I don't even want to articulate.

Surgery (yuck) is on Tuesday morning. Greg should be in the hospital only three or so days. We will get a preliminary pathology report right after the surgery and our final one about a week later.

I want to keep saying thank you and it just does not convey what is in my heavy and lightened heart.

August 27

NANCY'S CARINGBRIDGE LETTER

I have a thank you card that says, "Thank You" in 15 different languages. If I learn all of those, could it possibly convey our appreciation of each of you and of this beautiful world of which we are a part?

Twenty-two years today of being married to this lovely man who is a hero to so many.

August 28

NANCY'S CARINGBRIDGE LETTER

Saturday morning – countdown time now.

We leave tomorrow, and we will take the girls to a concert that they bought tickets for months ago. Greg and I are dropping them off and picking them up. Then we drive to Corvallis, leave Lilly for Freshman orientation and drive back to Seattle on Monday night just in time for Greg's 5:30 am date with the neurosurgeon.

"Walking the plank" comes to mind as the feelings reveal themselves. We know we are in good hands with our surgeon. I will be visualizing his skilled hands as he does all he can to get this nasty beast out of Greg's brain.

Greg is on one of his morning jaunts today...he has a friend whom he has woken up at 6:30 every morning this week. It has been deeply sweet. The guys have coffee and breakfast. Then today he goes for a Reiki session.

We are thankful for this week at home, although it feels surreal that it has only been a week. It grounds us with all that is familiar, real, inspirational, sustaining, warm, and secure. We are filled up. Cards, hugs, love expressed in every way imaginable, natural beauty, healing sauna, dog time, time for kids to see friends and business details *ad nauseum*.

This tumor has become a full-time job. Each day I have a long list to accomplish and yesterday I even finished it. I hope I will have more time today to be outside and quiet.

Tomorrow our Quaker meeting is devoting our normal Sunday morning time for a "Holding the Ewerts in the Light" meeting, which we will be able to attend.

Our anniversary dinner last night was sweet and also bittersweet...we know we can only be in the moment now but we can't stop knowing why the moment feels the way it does. We are taken care of on so many levels and we never understood that. In a week, the word "love" has taken both of us places with each other and our community that we did not ever know existed. It is deep and it is powerful.

And the tornado warning siren is still sounding in my deepest being. I pray for courage to enter this. That is all I have prayed for this week – courage for all of us. My task in life is to be able to gracefully and faithfully embrace what I am given. It is not about what we get but how we deal with what we get. Now is my time to learn what that means.

I am sad today that our life, as we have known it, is no more. It has been such a good one. I know that this new life is just as unknown and full of potential as the one Greg and I vowed to live twenty-two years ago. No one can know what those wedding vows will mean. It is evident that we did not know how our two lives, which became five, could and would merge and thrive in this unbelievable community of hearts both here on our island and afar.

August 28

CLARA'S CARINGBRIDGE LETTER

Hey everyone,

Thank you so much for all the sweet comments. As all of us know, my dad's surgery is on the 31st, this Tuesday. Gray is the color of support for brain cancer, and though many of you may already be doing this, if you could wear gray that day in honor of my dad, it would hopefully add to all the warm thoughts people are sending out, and amount to a good result. Or the best in the situation that we've been given. Also, there is a site that has t-shirts in support of brain cancer and I am going to post the link, so that if any of you are interested, you can purchase one.

August 28

NANCY'S JOURNAL

Today I found the "wailing wall." It is a beach that looks out over the water – waters on which we have had many a family adventure with Greg smiling at the helm.

I cried and wailed and not a soul heard me. Oh, how I needed it.

August 28th

GREG'S CARINGBRIDGE LETTER

Of course, on our island rumors fly so I want you to know I am alive and well with just two tumors not four and the extent will be determined on Tuesday and Nancy did not have to carry me down the mountain after collapsing in a heap. I am still being obnoxious as ever, talk too much and presently feel great. I plan on coming to school the week following my surgery to talk to the middle school students about what is going on and so they understand what a brain tumor really is and how it is treated and why am not there.

I am planning on getting rid of this tumor through love, modern medicine, visualization, hitting myself in the head with a hammer -whatever it takes!!

I am SO moved by all your support – that alone should take the tumor out – however I have not cancelled my surgery date – I am keeping that as a safety measure!

August 29

NANCY'S JOURNAL

Sagging, sad morning as we get ready for the hospital. Collecting items for an altar...his and mine: the NW Indian button blanket of the grizzly, dirt from the sanctuary floor of the church in Chimayo, NM (where I was only two months ago), whatever else will help us. Red toe nail polish for me?

Clara in tears last night—the printer wouldn't print. It's not about the printer. She has been way stronger and more attentive and sensitive than a 15 year old should have to be. I have not been as careful with her as she needed. God, this is hard. I honestly don't know if I can do it, if I can be all I need to be.

I don't like leaving my home. I never like it under any circumstances. I sure don't like it now.

August 30

GREG'S CARINGBRIDGE LETTER

Morning ramblings...

Sitting in Denny'a off the freeway – America. One of our our islandian expressions is "We are going to America." I am here after looking for the logger's breakfast hole in historic downtown Chehalis. Does not exist. James Thurber wrote so poignantly for the New Yorker on time in the late 50's from his sweet spot in rural Maine. He wrote that after the television networks extended their evening programming until 10:00 in the evening, the little farmer cafes did not open until 6:00 am (an our later than they used to) – too late for a true farmer! (That was before anybody stayed up for 24 hours besides Jack Kerouac and Timothy Leary!

Picked up our two girls from the Vampire Weekend Concert (old folks like me thought they were going to suck each others blood!) – one so crestfallen she could not speak ("can't I have one thing go right in my life?") and the older sister more philosophical about the concert being canceled because one of the group members was sick. Down I-5 in the night headed to Corvallis – Lilly's registration at OSU – found the Relax Inn at 11:00pm. Wouldn't you think people could think of more creative names for motels??? I always like the "Dew Drop Inn – probably owned by a former TOYS R US employee!

SO I ordered my usual American breakfast – two poached eggs, (to see how badly they can screw up poached eggs), sourdough, (I always order sourdough because it makes me think of the early men that roamed this county with their sourdough starter), sausage (pigs are good) and hash brown as (midwest boy brought up on potatoes). Just now a young man just came up to me and asked "Mac book pro?" Yeah – "I never got used to the platform. but i love my Iphone" I reply – "Steve Jobs is brilliant – If I was that smart I would not be sitting here at Denny's getting my 'Build your own!'" He said "I would still be here – I love Denny's!" I guess I am truly in America.

I am carrying the warmth and love of 50 people surrounding us at Quaker meeting yesterday. Thank you for the tears and laughter. Note; (Too funny – the classic Denny's waiter just said, "Sorry about the wait – the cook is just trying to get the poached eggs right. He had to make them four times." (Not kidding!)

The door of the hospital looms in front of me – I am not afraid – I understand technology. My surgeon is good and will do what is necessary. What I don't know is what is on the other side – will it have the vibrance of this amazing week??? It can not help but be different – we will know more about the journey we are on – the fight we are fighting. This week I could just be...what changes are in store for me now??

LIfe is good, even with the last bite of my potatoes which I am sure are really taken from a paper shredder and sprayed with potato flavoring.

I just have to say, I love living.

August 30

NANCY'S CARINGBRIDGE LETTER

It has been a day. Leaving Lilly at her university orientation was harder than when she clung to me as I left her for two weeks of camp at age seven. This is just for two days but it is the two days.

Lots of realities hitting home as we drive along, getting information about how long surgery will be and hearing again, "four to five hours." We work hard to keep terror at bay, and then we get our messages and once again, are lifted with laughter, tears, hope, and courage. Thank you, dear friends. It is enormous.

Greg is eating an entire pint of Ben and Jerry's Crème Brûlée without regard to his high cholesterol count or supposed dairy intolerance.

Later, we stopped at the Sorrento hotel, a short walk from the hotel where we are staying.

I got a glass of scotch and water, short on water. Greg, ginger ale. Clara, some African tea and a bread pudding "on the house" – did they sense our trauma???

Lovely mahogany walls, soft furniture, sighs of relief to be off the highway and on this new "super highway." We will get there. We are at peace with our next steps and looking forward to sleep.

August 30

Greg's CaringBridge Letter

Just returned from the Sorrento Hotel – a place of peace and beauty. I carry all of you and the spirit of the Grizzly with me...(we toasted to that Griz tonight)

Thank you all...I feel peaceful. Talk to you tomorrow afternoon.

August 31

Nancy's CaringBridge Letter

It is early morning. Greg woke Clara up and they just headed out for an early morning city walk together.

Sleep was not peaceful or plentiful last night; it was that kind of restless sleep where you wake up and feel like your heart is beating too fast. And that kind of wake up where you know something is wrong as your body and psyche move into the reality of the day.

I am off to have a city walk myself and find a good cup of tea.

Yesterday, a bad cup of tea on the road resulted in a big pout from me. I said "I have not asked for that much, but there is one thing true of me. I can get through just about anything if I have had a good cup of tea."

August 31

GREG'S CARINGBRIDGE LETTER

Clara walked a little of my personal Seattle history with me this morning – making hundreds of cinnamon rolls at the Bakery Cafe, windows open, early morning in the summer – slipping rolls to the homeless. Sitting at Lowell's Cafe with CLara telling stories, laughing, talking about music and the 60's.

Great vision of this tumor getting knocked out of my head and being run over by a bus.

August 31

NANCY'S JOURNAL

Sitting and waiting in the hospital lobby. So many images: Greg having his head shaved, Greg in the OR – light all over him. Will the surgeon see his spirit? I would not want him to be distracted by such a powerful spirit so I guess it is better that he just does his job. I am in the moment. Right now is all that matters – and love.

So hard to leave Greg this morning, to let go of his warmth, his body. When I see him next, what will I see? It is so scary. I have his wedding ring on my finger next to mine.

I am envisioning light and love around him.

August 31

Nancy's CaringBridge Letter

I have a glass of red wine, a bowl of spinach pea soup and a piece of crunchy, whole-wheat bread. I am beyond tired, beyond exhausted and very appreciative of the thoughtful nourishment, both physical and spiritual, from the best friends anyone could ever ask for. I think I will have a PhD in thoughtfulness if I can just remember the incredible gestures offered by all of you.

Greg has woken up from surgery. Are there words to describe Greg on narcotics? He embarrassed himself – no, me – enough with the hospital staff. I won't do any more damage to his reputation here. I will tell stories privately someday, but for now, he was loquacious with more than a few expletives as the general theme (and I was once worried about my language during childbirth?)

We talked to the surgeon after the surgery, and we still have more questions than answers. Bottom line is, the tumor could be stage 4 glioblastoma or a lymphoma of some kind. We know what might be the future if it is a glioblastoma. There are indicators pointing to the possibility of lymphoma, which was a surprise to us. We will not know for sure until about a week from now. In general, this could be good news because some lymphomas are more treatable than glioblastomas.

Only about 30% of the tumor could be removed because it is right under the motor strip. The treatment to try to eradicate the tumor is radiation and chemo, which will begin after he recovers from the surgery.

We feel relieved that the surgery is over and we can move on to the next steps. Greg looks good, which is great to see. His face looks relaxed and peaceful and, thanks to the drugs, he feels good. He won't have a lot of pain from this and if things go well, we might be able to come home in three days.

Lilly got back from her OSU registration just in time to see Greg after surgery. So now Clara, Lilly and I are happy in our little hotel room with our kitchenette and good food.

CHAPTER 2

SEPTEMBER 2010

Be grateful for whoever comes,
because each has been sent
us a guide from beyond.

—Rumi, "The Guest House"

September 1

NANCY'S CARINGBRIDGE LETTER

It has been a hard morning. Greg has more left side paralysis, which is discouraging. He had hoped that with the removal of the tumor, the pressure would be relieved and he would have functioning return. We know there is swelling and physical therapy will be able to improve this. But reality is sinking in and that reality is very difficult.

Our angel friend Terri is here now and she is a PT. She is talking to Greg and has some good words to help him feel optimistic about how he will work with this...brain pathways rerouting, etc.

(Later in the afternoon)

Time takes on such a different reality in this place. We stayed with Greg all morning, not getting to eat breakfast until noon.

Greg is feeling better but nothing can take the reality of the tumor away. He had a visit from OT and PT today and he walked a bit. Left side paralysis continues.

Last night, Greg had the nurse from hell, did not have his needs met, could not sleep and then had a visit from the neurosurgeon this morning – all before I could get over to him. I have not been able to talk to the surgeon myself today, but apparently, he told Greg that there were more "dead" cells than he had originally thought, which points to the glioblastoma, which was hard to hear. Of course, we still don't know until we know.

September 2

NANCY'S JOURNAL

Hard night last night. I pray for courage to have what it takes to face this and all that it entails.

My heart is breaking.

September 2

CLARA'S CARINGBRIDGE LETTER

Hello everyone,

I am just letting everyone know that we are trying to make 1000 cranes for my dad. He needs all the luck he can get. I have been making some at the hospital and have found it rather therapeutic, because you can just hone in on it, and go through the motions. If you don't know how to make a crane, you can ask someone you know, or look it up online. If you do make any cranes you can drop them by our house or send them to us.

The support has been wonderfully overwhelming.

September 2

NANCY'S CARINGBRIDGE LETTER

I am sitting with Greg in his new room with a view of clear blue skies over the city as I take dictation from him:

"Reality of entering the medical world hit hard last night. Slept with my Grizzly Button Blanket over me and got some needed rest. Nancy and the girls are godsends. The frustration of a left hand not working, the reality of fighting this tumor with radiation and chemo and all that will take is suddenly looming large. The only way to do it is one step at a time. Doctor Lee said I could go outside today. Breakfast is oatmeal, brown sugar and half-and-half, preceded by a latte delivered by Nancy. Somehow my high cholesterol has taken on less significance. Clara and Lilly got haircuts yesterday...strikingly beautiful daughters. Lilly snuggled with me while I lay in my button blanket last night. Her job today is to shave the other side of my head while Clara gathers cranes.

I am humbled by your care and I need it.

Today grief for our losses and our changed life seems to be marching in....We have made it through the mechanical parts. Home tomorrow… what will it bring?

September 2

NANCY'S CARINGBRIDGE LETTER

Another day with a few visitors. Finished shaving Greg's head. Lilly and Clara headed back to our island with a friend. I had a bit of time alone, which was balm for my soul. I found St. James cathedral quiet and peaceful. I lit a candle for all of us. Now Greg and I are having dinner together in the hospital room.

After dinner, I can take him outside in the wheelchair for a breath of fresh air.

September 3

NANCY'S CARINGBRIDGE LETTER

Greg had the nurse call me on the hotel phone to ask me to come over about 6 a.m. He is worlds better today and I had a feeling that he was calling because he had changed his mind and wanted to go home. I was right! Greg feels much better this morning and seems more normal in his psyche. The idea of home sends alluring rays of comfort.

I am watching the sunrise over the city. I am so not a city girl. I hate the noise — no one seems to be able to do anything in a city anymore without a loud machine – but at least Seattle has water to look at and we have a view of Lake Union outside of the window. Greg wanted me to write this note and reflect his thoughts and our mutual conversation about it all this morning, so this is from both of us.

Living in this world of the hospital for days has offered us just a small view into a myriad of lives. Even though I came into this experience with a lot of familiarity with hospital life from my former career, I now see it all with completely new eyes.

I walk down the halls and am aware that every person in every room has a story of their own, filled with uncertainty, pain, hope, grief, worry, courage and ripples that one can only imagine. Greg befriended his CCU "roommate" who had just had a 12-hour surgery (They talked through the curtain in the night...It was the "nurse ratchet night"), and he wanted me to take her a copy of Kindred Spirits after they were both moved onto other floors. I found her, delivered the book and we had such a sweet talk. Here she is with her husband and children in their own real-life drama and she was concerned about us.

And then there are the employees; oh, what lives they all come from. Last night there was the Filipino aide who was a former marine and helped Greg with the urinal using his "marine-type" personality, which was not pleasant, but then noticed the unusual piece of fruit brought by a friend, and with utter delight, he told Greg all about it: a "Vietnamese Watermelon – they cost $5.00, but they are the best you can ever eat." He softened with memories of another time.

Then there is the aide who is a single mom and has to leave her 12 year old, ADD son at home with her mother so she can work as much as possible to earn a living to support them. She wants so much to find the best for her son in the complicated public-school system and medical world. Hours earlier Greg's internist was here and they talked about her son who just started private school in Seattle so he can get the best education possible. They both play an equal role in taking care of Greg, but the disparity of their options is glaringly evident.

Hospitals hold a world of humanity, exposed and brought into focus by the vulnerability inherent in this experience.

September 3

NANCY'S CARINGBRIDGE LETTER

I am in the hospital cafeteria with the memory of sitting here with Lilly, Clara and Emma only two week ago, stunned, freaked out, knowing we needed to eat. Could really have only been two weeks ago? I honestly just looked at a calendar to confirm my disbelief. We, almost literally, have walked a lifetime in two weeks. Greg has seen, felt and been honored hearing the impact he has had on people, and the word's "powerful gift" just seem so small when I see his lovely face and twinkling eyes as he hears each tribute, story and words of love.

I am very attuned now to the kindness of strangers; I have never been in a place where this has been more meaningful and evident. The cars that stop and wave me across a busy street, the cashier who smiles, the cafeteria employee here who just reminded me to put my charge card back in my wallet (gee, wish she could just ride on my shoulder!), the nice nurses, the bossy/kind waitress at the restaurant the other night, the manager at the Verizon store. It goes on and on. Do we ever have any idea of our impact on others? It is massive.

I am beginning to believe that just these simple acts of kindness could change the world. The impact is that strong. Conversely, on the few occasions that someone has not been helpful I have had to work hard to control myself. I just want to scream, "Really, do you need to act like this? Do you know how it feels?" The girls look at me hesitantly, "Uh oh, don't say it, Mom. Just leave it and walk away." I guess they know the potential all too well!

Off I go to pack up while Greg is sleeping peacefully. It will be a long day.

September 4

GREG'S CARINGBRIDGE LETTER

Saturday morning -on finer typing – just to say home last night n the 9:50 ferry – thank you So much Molly and Steven.For me ret an d recovery – escaped the hospital feeing that you will never get well.Now meetings and plans for treatmentThere is something unusual about my cancer tissue as it has been sent to the U and we will hear in about a week. Discouraging dealing with an unresponsive left hand. I have to admit the scar is impressive – you get what you pay forat Vitginia Mason.though a new car would probably cost less and be more practical

Thank you al for flowers,c cranes, notes and support

September 4

NANCY'S CARINGBRIDGE LETTER

It has been a busy day trying to unpack and tidy up and get some things organized. Everything takes so long. Greg slept a lot today but I did not. The girls took off for Bumpershoot Music Festival, I took a good walk, and we had a lovely dinner delivered. The dishes are done and I feel a bit more together as I head to bed.

Before that, however, I have important news to share – Greg moved his thumb and fingers tonight! It was just a little but it is monumental. Every one of us has been telling him that as the swelling decreases, his functioning will return but who really knows? Now we have proof. It is exciting and a boost for him.

It is wonderful to be home. The air is exquisite, the dogs are both snoring as I write, and today I looked out through the clearest windows I have ever seen. A window-washing angel came while we were gone. This is a luxury that was unimaginable to me and it is heavenly. I went outside to empty the garbage and someone had taken all of our garbage and recycling to the dump, and I found the wood split and stacked. Good heavens, I have never felt so indulged. Thank you, our islandians, for your thoughtfulness. And for all of you far away, I know you would all be here doing the same if you could! It makes such a difference to me.

I am really tired and ready for good sleep. The phone rang tonight and all we heard was really loud music in the background. It was Clara calling from Bob Dylan's concert at Bumpershoot. She called us just so we could hear him for a minute. How funny is that? Our 15 year-old going to hear Bob Dylan while her tired old parents stay home.

September 5

GREG'S CARINGBRIDGE LETTER

okay I am up again early – not correcting mistakes sorry -slept most of yesterday – so glad to sit outside breathe lopez air without anyone checking my blood pressure or poking me with needles. i can just whip iy out and pee on the grass – no one shoving a urinal up my stylish hospital pants telling me to pee – a kind of freedom. yes some movement for me restrained joy because I know what I want to be doing. learning patience.

Some fear about what is ahead – I have always had so much to do – now just days of rest but I guess in a week once we find out what our next step is it will feel different.

Since I do have an audience larger than 20 middle schoolers in a math class kind of listening I would like to say again how I wish I had lived my life saying more what I really felt and had asked more for what I wanted. I was the third child of five and my job was to make peace out of chaos – to soften tensions. My wish for us all is to speakers of our truths.

Good morning!

September 5

NANCY'S CARINGBRIDGE LETTER

Home takes on this false feeling of normalcy. It is alluring and comforting. I now recognize denial as a strong, soothing opiate – a nice friend to hang around with for a few days. On one level, neither Greg nor I are in denial, and on another level, we can't possibly stay in that, "Oh this tragedy is happening to us," place.

It has been strange to be completely focused on our little world and my part in it, at the exclusion of most everything else. It is unlike me. Last week I decided to just give myself a week to be self-involved. Ironically, yesterday it began to feel natural again to be curious about other people and reach out a bit.

This morning I notice a more familiar feeling of energy. It feels good. But at the same time, I feel like I am walking in new shoes that someone else ordered and they don't really fit, but I must wear them all the time. They aren't awful shoes but they are not what I would have chosen.

September in our household has always been intense with the girls starting school, Greg working constantly, me going back to work – the big shift of September. Now I look at the calendar and (hmm) a bigger "big shift," but into what? We can't fathom it now. We have a second child leaving for college in two weeks! Under other circumstances, that would be monumental. It still is, but there is so much else that is even more monumental. How does one live with monumental all the time and still be just the same old people?

All of a sudden, and it is really sudden, we have to totally redefine our hopes and dreams, our definition of family and just about everything else. And then there is that looming phone call which can come any day. Then we face many more fateful moments.

It becomes pretty easy to live in the now because beyond now is so incredibly unfamiliar and unknown that I have little desire to know or fantasize about it. Only three weeks ago, we were imagining living overseas for a year again and now what do we dream about? What a completely different way to view our world.

I wish I could adequately describe how your love and support feels. Kind of like a huge pillow that we can just sink into. Maybe that is why this so often does not feel nearly as dreadful as I would have imagined it, or maybe also that good pal of mine, Denial, is speaking. But honestly, the real nightmare would be life without the pillow. Thank you our dear friends, near and far, for being the pillow.

September 5

EMMA'S CARINGBRIDGE LETTER

After a phone call from home this morning, I wanted to let everyone know how much I appreciate everything people have done and said! Being in Montreal the past week has been unspeakably hard, especially during the surgery. Wanting to be there with my family, and to have that support around me, wanting to be able to see my dad (I did finally have a chance to check out his new hair-do last night over Skype!).

Even though there have been some incredibly sad moments, I have been able to go through the guestbook on this site and read the many wonderful, caring things people have to say, and this has really helped me feel like I too have so much support and love behind me.

Thank you all for being there.

September 7

GREG'S CARINGBRIDGE LETTER

Happy birthday Mom! s painted her nails crimnson the night before. her body knotted in the fetal position racked by artrithisis and died.Sshe would have been 90 years old this year though a Halloween night took her away many years ago. I learned how to get through life "on a wing and a pray" from her.

Tonight -little sleep — girls rocking out at bumbershoot, the driver Lilly) crying phone call for mom(Are cell phones really helpful?) — just enough to set off the worry section of the brain(mine must be there!) No they are bringing three more our island kids back to the ferry — not in the parent plan book and the comforting irritated voice "don'y worry — be happy!)

Of course as

i write this all five are packed in the Toyota sleeping in the ferry line and I am still trying to get back on track.

Very little sleep last night – wrong meds? Who knows. On my open schedule Isleep when I want to.

Huck and I will celebrate a note of freedom by having coffee in the village at 10.

Yesterday my P.T. appointment consisted of learning to play ping pong using my left hand – picking it with my crude claw and throwing it up to serve How fun was that- especially playing with"Biba"- normally a peaceful kind soul but akiller around a table. We generally play fairly evenly where i win about 70 % of the time(sans tumor). So in our P.T. practice she professionally noted my right side reaction was slightly compromised Finally being the competitors we are we agreed to play one game where I could throw up the serve with my right hand. she has to anyway because of only two digits on onee hand! and well on our island!

The epic battle began and ended with a tough overtime victory for me 24-22!Teri was even going after my newly discovered weaker side -I can see I will need to client privileges to see what she writes down in her medical records. Ping – pong therapy is aiive and well on our island!

good morning

September 7

NANCY'S JOURNAL

Worry, worry, worry – about our kids, about Greg being awake in the night, his speech changes, what we will know, what we won't know, the decisions we have to make, and the aggravation of rain drops on my clean windows. I am going for a walk and that will help. The girls made it back safe and sound. Sometimes we are both afraid and it is all too big.

September 8

GREG'S CARINGBRIDGE LETTER

Given a beautiful quilt yesterday by the our island School Staff – made in only one week. Sleep does not come easily again – I wrap myself in the new quilt = ever grateful. Life is so vivid right now – colors, taste, people. I am lost in the beauty -yet I soon will be in the airport security line with a ticket to an unknown destination about to get on the medical conveyor belt to be scanned, analyzed, classified and treated and may never get to where I want to go and be.

I feel like I have a small window of peace right now before I am handed a ticket.

Good morning!Why isn't everyone up! Time is passing by!(just kidding really!)

September 8

NANCY'S CARINGBRIDGE LETTER

We got news today and the tumor is a Glioblastoma Stage 4. It is not a good diagnosis. We will go to Seattle on September 15th for Radiation Oncology consult.

We pray for courage and as much quality of life as we can muster – that will be the miracle.

Emma is with her roommates and planning to come home a weekend in October. It is hard news to bear from afar. We are a family in deep grief tonight and grateful for each other. We cry, we rage, we hold each other with love.

September 9

GREG'S CARINGBRIDGE LETTER

I have no words tonight -shattered . I will sleep by my grizzly candle sent to me from my high school girlfriend, Mary (also the P.T.) who taught me how sweet your first love can be. I want that grizzly spirit to fight for my right hand, my voice, my vision – I do not want to travel down this road.

Tonight I rage against the dying of the light.

September 10

GREG'S CARINGBRIDGE LETTER

Tonight I honor the lovely men in my life who gathered around the firelight last to hold me inin their hearts and ask what do I need and listen to my pain. I dance in and out of this reality only get slapped in the face as I say good night to my daughters and tell them I love them. I feeling lif'e's vibrance and feeling deeply content tonight. The grizzly bear who has been working so hard is sleeping for a moment.

First oncology meeting tomorrow – sister Jane coming up from San Francisco some important question will be answered.

Good Morning! call someone who has ben on the"B" list today!

September 11

GREG'S CARING BRIDGE LETTER

The future which was cruelly ripped from me three weeks ago was returned yesterday in a modified form by the staff at Seattle Cancer

Alliance – hope really =long term prognosis not good but fear of bed rid-den with a feeding tube can be held at by while I have some quality of life.

i awoke griz tihis morning to fight to keep what I have now, a good right hand, the ability to drive on our island only, foul language, ability to talk and keep find some humor in it all,bring surrounded by prayers and love, a lovely wife, fabulous kids, a sister who was willing to pop on a plane at the last second to be at the meeting, friends willing to crawl under the house to find the dead rat smell(and the rat!), amazing food delivered to our door so we can be dealing with what seems like a million details all the while holding each other in our washes of disbelief and pain.

Soon we will join the lopez cancer car club for radiation and chemo and head probably Everett for treatment with new hope I may have a number of months where I may feel reasonable good!

this morning I am seeing a bit of a silver lining around the tumor cloud not unlike the first griz I saw hiking alone at 21, near to the wild heart of life, on a late afternoon in Jasper National Park,low sun back-lighting its' golden fur – two almost full grown cubs wandering behind – that was when she charged me and chose to acutally circle around me and let me live another day.

NOW I will asking my griz every day to just give me tomorrow!

Good morning! This morning I so grateful for my sisters and brother and a sweet email from my father. now 95,,struggling to stay alive in his battle with cancer – food delivered through a tube – quality of life ripped from him a few short months ago. Life clearly some times has cruel iro-nies.

September 11

NANCY'S CARINGBRIDGE LETTER

Sleep is such a panacea. For all those hours of sleep, I get a break from the intensity of our lives; I don't have to think about a clinical trial, I don't have to make a decision, wash a dish, hear the phone or attend to anyone else. Of course, the best of it is that when I sleep, I have energy to face it all when I wake up.

We have been frustrated this week waiting to hear from Group Health about appointments and can't meet with them until next week. Meanwhile, we got some helpful information and our second opinion from Seattle Cancer Care Alliance. SCCA is an amazing place. It feels like a Disneyland for cancer patients. As soon as you walk in the door, you see all sorts of folks without hair, using walking devices, you name it, but all are treated with great respect and consideration. There is juice and water available, the offer to validate the parking instead of charging for it, and they untold resources offered to us. This was all before we met the doctor!

Without unneeded detail, our visit gave us the information that our prescribed course of treatment, which GH will recommend later this week, is just what we should do now.

And as Greg said, the medical staff there also predicted that Greg will feel tired, but in general, quality of life should be about what it is now. There is the hope that the treatment will stop tumor growth for a while. It was gratifying to be able to ask questions and get answers. There is more to figure out but at least we have someone to ask questions of. They gave us emails, phone numbers and offered to work with whatever other doctors we end up with.

There is no question that the tumor is large, and that it can't be removed surgically. How much effect radiation and chemo can have and for how long is not predictable and this is the harsh reality.

When we returned home, the house was full of good food and a bunch of teenagers! It was an evening of feeling normal for a while.

Greg, Jane and I hid out in the back room and talked while the kids took over the kitchen and hot tub. It was a sweet, relaxed evening.

Lilly will leave in a week for college. Greg's freeway driving seemed a bit compromised yesterday, so I think it will be me driving for a while.

We are fed every day with food, love, cards, flowers, angels who clean refrigerators, find dead rats, encourage us to travel after treatment is over, procure plane tickets, and help in ways I don't even know about. I continue to be amazed and in awe.

September 12

NANCY'S JOURNAL

So many tears today. I guess it is good we live on an island because there is so much water to absorb them.

I try to be optimistic and hopeful and yet I relive my days a year ago, when I was helping my friend with the same tumor. Her glioblastoma was also not surgically removable, and she died three months later. How to be hopeful and realistic? It is so very painful.

September 13

GREG'S CARINGBRIDGE LETTER

Nancy and I had a sweet walk on the beach – sorted, cried,watched the waves – what we have been dealt has so many layers of complexity – the tumor is at the center. Nancy, my girls, myself – we all are having to dance with this beast in our own way... And that is constantly changing. My girls are strong, beautiful – I wish they did not have to get on this dance floor. As a family we are together in this battle.

September 13

NANCY'S CARINGBRIDGE LETTER

Sleep was welcome last night after my deep sobbing yesterday. Before I went to bed I decided to explore some blogs of glioblastoma survivors. I wanted to read stories of cases like Greg's but did not find any.

What I did find was a lot of blogs that started with an "In Memoriam" page. I quickly decided that sleep was a better option.

This morning I succeeded in taking a hard, fast walk. It is therapeutic for me. I wanted to be alone and I had some powerful revelations. One is that, regardless of what is happening now, if I had the choice, I would not go back to my former life. How can I say that? I never even dreamed I would feel the deep sadness, fear and rage that I experience readily now.

And yet I can honestly say that I have never felt love as I do now. Once, I heard passion described as that profound love that mothers feel after childbirth and the moment I heard that description I knew what she meant. I feel that passion now. I feel it for Greg and I feel it for my children. I am grateful to know this deep love. I want to declare it so I will always remember it. It is profound to be the recipient of so much love. How does this happen? Why us?

September 15

NANCY'S CARINGBRIDGE LETTER

I had a day with Clara and Lilly off island for the orthodontist and some nice time together. I came home to dirty dishes and reorganizing so we can leave again early tomorrow. Greg had a wonderful Reiki treatment tonight while I puttered around the house.

I am sure I am losing my mind. I have a library book that I lost in the house last week and finally found it under my bed. I really want to read it but have not gotten past page one. Now I can't find it again, and I know it is almost due back to the library. It is a rather large book. How can I keep losing it when I have not even been able to read it? Obviously, this is a "symptom," but will the library understand?

September 16

NANCY'S CARINGBRIDGE LETTER

What a day! We had two good visits at Group Health today: one with Radiation Oncology and the other with Medical Oncology. They answered some zillion questions, were compassionate, considerate and as encouraging as they can be at this time.

Each person seemed competent and they bent over backwards to help us get started soon. While we talked at length about clinical trials, the course of action recommended by everyone we have seen is radiation and oral chemo. This is a well-tested regime that has proven to stop tumor growth for a period of time.

At this point, we do not see the value of racing off to some other location for a clinical trial. We have decided we will do the treatment in Seattle, which will be five days a week for six weeks.

Feels good to be home tonight and to have one whole day tomorrow before we head off again on Friday. It was a 13-hour day today, door to door, and we walked into a freshly cleaned house, a delicious dinner provided by another angel, and another who took my laundry off the line. It literally makes all the difference in the world. There is the Angel of Crowfoot Farms and the "tea in the mail" angel and the hand-designed journal angel.

What a heavenly host! Now if the "angel who finds lost library books" would just visit tomorrow, that would really be great!

September 17

GREG'S CARINGBRIDGE LETTER

Nancy's journal entry covered the mechanical details of our next step of treatment. I am happy to have a plan developed and anxious to get started on treatment knowing that it could help improve my functioning and kill the cancer cells. The harsh reality is that there is a tumor in my head and sometimes that reality hits pretty hard. The other news that was especially difficult to hear was the recommendation that I don't drive on the freeway; that I bicycle with a partner, or only row a boat if someone is with me and I wear a life jacket. To top it off, when I asked the

Doctor about shooting rabbits, he suggested that I should not be shooting a gun (not sure if he was really concerned about the rabbits or the people around) "Do you have neighbors?" he asked.

(Transcriber's Note: At this point in the conversation, I could see in his eyes that we had quickly switched from peace-loving our islandians to NRA members. I did my best to convince him otherwise...hope it worked.)

I then asked about flying my plane, he just rolled his eyes! I took that as a "no". My fierce independence is being slowly chopped away as concerns for safety get added. The reality of what I can't do is harder to swallow than the number of pills I am asked to take!

Yesterday, however, I had the best ping pong therapy session. I felt limber, my reactions are returning and my hand is to continuing to show improvement-very encouraging. Fortunately this followed a tough morning of feeling Mr. Tumor's presence – feeling angry as I drop things, and lose an hour and half of typing due to my fingers not working right – I can't escape it and have bring the tumor to my table.

I have had a lot of time to reflect on my teaching career- I have been totally overwhelmed by the number of people, (parents and students) offering love, support and telling me the specific ways I have been an effective teacher. This has led me to musing in the early mornings about the "art of teaching". Here are some thoughts.

During my last quarter of Architecture school in the early 70s, I volunteered at AS1 – a crazy, wonderful alternative school in Seattle. The students there had amazing freedom to do what they wanted – there was a stunning creative, chaotic spirit in the school. Back then in 1971, many of us rode on some great trains that did not run on straight tracks – My track was to join an art's community (in an old Frat building) focusing on photography and reading everything I could about alternative education.

I was intrigued with the idea of adding choice, freedom and community to a classroom.

The early 70's was really a renaissance of education and Seattle was the center of that movement. I decided to become a teacher by getting a degree from Pacific Oaks College which ran a program through The Little School in Bellevue. The Little School was run by a radical, lovely, white haired "Jewish mother", Eleanor Siegel. The school's location was adjacent to 9 acres of woods and was not unlike Summerhill in England. Kids could built forts in the woods every day all day if they wanted – and damn it the kids still learned to read and write somehow!

I was hired at the Little School and worked there for four wonderful years as new teacher. During this time I learned and the real meaning of "teachable moments" i.e. catching kids when they are ready to learn. The other important aspect of the Little School was the establishment of "community" in each class. We would sit in a circle each morning and talk about what was happening that day and any concerns kids had. We did actually set some of the day for structured learning.

This is when I also started my first backpack trip to the ocean – 1977. The Little School gave me the opportunity to test my belief that through rugged outdoor adventures kids learn to work together, create new friendships and discover a confidence and self reliance they would not otherwise find. This was the beginning of 30 years of trips with kids to the ocean.

From there I went to Lakeside School (private school in Seattle and Bill Gates alma mater) and taught math in the middle school for 5 years. It was a great job – small classes, teachers not as overloaded, time to meet with individual students built into the day – really pure teaching, and of course extremely bright kids. However, I found the way I approached the kids and the classroom was similar to the Little School but in a dramatically different setting. I even wore the occasional tie and was called "Mr. Greg" instead of just "Greg". In the end I learned that education is about relationships, creating challenging mental and physical adventures and love.

In the late 80s a teaching opportunity came up in the San Juan Islands and I this enabled me to follow my dream of living on our island and here I am.

I have been trying to figure out why there is such out pouring of love and support coming my way when, really, I was just doing a job that I loved in the best way I knew how. I can be a bit scattered, shoot from the hip, not follow all the rules, not have all the paperwork in, and have trouble finding things -but through this website, cards and letters your comments noting specific examples of things I have done, I realize I accomplished in my teaching what I set out to do. I have developed lasting friendships with students based on mutual caring and respect. I think I have helped students learn to love learning.

When I got my pilot's license two yeas ago (THAT was hard work!), the instructor's parting words were: "Now you have a license to learn". I love that. If I have instilled in kids a desire and feeling that they now have their own "license to learn", I am content.

All to say – thank you for all that has come back to me – It really has been humbling and it gives me a deep inner peace.

Of course the paradox is that it takes an element of tragedy, something as dramatic as a brian tumor to set this off. But I do truly understand how this has changed lives – our lives shifted when my friend, Hugh Lawrence passed away from the same disease. It was then that I started climbing mountains, sold everything that took time away from family and applied for the Fulbright teacher exchange to England which totally changed our lives. So if I can be the the catalyst for change, great! I just wish I could do it another way.

Our days slip between ultimate hope and the medical reality. Understand that I have to do the difficult dance with both. When the oncologist says average life expectancy with my particular tumor (based on location and lack of surgical options) is 12 months, I will not be sitting back and letting the time go by. We have made the best treatment choice for us. We want as much quality of life as we can get. We are working on a lot of details so my daughters and dear wife are taken care of. Being a math person I asked the oncologist "when does that 12 months begin?" He said "the day of surgery". I said, "That just bought me three weeks!" He said he would not charge extra. But then my daughter Emma reminds me regularly "Dad, you are NOT average!!"

Given all that l know, I am going to be filling my days with as much as I can and still fight for the miracle. We are planning a family trip before Christmas, a romantic get away for the two of us in February and of course, the annual "Dads and Kids" boat trip next summer!!!

thank you all – and to you teachers -the curriculum of love and compassion is more powerful than any textbook.

September 17

NANCY'S CARINGBRIDGE LETTER

Conversation in the Ewert household last night....

Nancy, desperate for answers:

"Lilly, have YOU by any chance seen my library book?

Lilly:

"Yeah, I turned it in to the library last week when you asked me to take that stuff by your bed!"

When I said "stuff," I meant DVDs— it never occurred to me

that she had taken the book too! Mystery solved...still looking for my passport since last February but I just applied for a new one!

September 21

GREG'S CARINGBRIDGE LETTER

The owl is out tonight – I probably will write rarely now – a new phase – treatment, Seattle, different energy as we move on. Still in shock but peaceful -I have been given amazing gifts – both tangible and spiritual. It is now my journey to walk with friends, strangers, and family. I take the hand of Nancy , my lovely wife who I love dearly and hand in hand until we have to let go – or maybe we never have to – that will not be up to us. I hold so close to my heart my three daughters – their spirits/souls are buried deep within me.

I am going to be riding on the back of the a Griz into the radiation for 35 days to beat this fucking thing and with the hope of roaming true griz country in Alaska many years from now. So I turn my fate over to the spirits that have always guided me – the mountains, the wind, the rain, the sea, the creatures of this beautiful earth that daily battle the fine line of life and death – it is that spirit I join them and maybe the griz or the raven or the coyote will give me a hand. The world is full of magic!

I have a deep belief that our soul lives after our body gives out – the soul to me is embodied in the ripples of energy, thoughts , feelings that pulsate through constantly from the love and spirit we give to the world.

So now I am ready to dance with whatever comes my way -bring it on!

September 30

NANCY'S CARINGBRIDGE LETTER

We survived Greg's first radiation day – 7-hours, door-to-door. Greg did not feel well so I drove the whole way down and back. During his treatment, I only had time for a quick trip into the grocery store (blissful anonymity) and a traveling latte.

I wonder if we will ever get over the "post-traumatic stress" of walking through the hospital's urgent care area, which offers us the grim reminder of the day our lives fell apart. It is all a bit stressful but once we got home, we had a beautiful afternoon and evening on our island. Greg took his first chemo pills before bed and seemed to tolerate them well. It is creepy swallowing a chemical strong enough to kill cancer cells. What a strange way to live.

It has been an emotional couple of days for our family. It is complicated to figure out the details of what nights we will stay in Seattle and when we will come home. We work to integrate visits from friends and family who live out of state; the emotional needs of our family, which rearrange themselves regularly; house projects here, because suddenly, Greg wants to finish loose ends; dog care; family travel; and the unique needs of the five of us. Yesterday it was too much. This morning, after a good night's sleep and the anticipation of a 9 am yoga class, it feels more manageable. I have always functioned better with a bit of predictability in my life but apparently that is a luxury of the past.

Lilly reports that she loves college life. It is Spirit Week at our island High School and today is "Dress like a teacher" day. Clara went to school dressed like Greg from head to toe.

September 30

GREG'S CARINGBRIDGE LETTER

A quick note – even though my head is pinned down and you can only breathe through a nose hole it is only ten minutes and I just go off into another world. Now i have done 2 – only 33 to go! and both days i git back by 12:45 and had the beautiful sunny afternoon on our island – even mowed the lawn this afternoon as this spell of Indian summer is making the grass grow like springtime! great techs and I know with this treatment the tumor is shrinking – worth the commute!

CHAPTER 3

OCTOBER 2010

. . . there was a new voice
which you slowly
recognized as your own

—Mary Oliver, "The Journey"

October 5

GREG'S CARINGBRIDGE LETTER

A quick update – treatment, though time consuming, is going well. No side effects so far and through breathing just being relaxed, the dreaded blue mask is okay.

I have now accepted not being able to drive on the freeway – possible but unlikely seizure. However, accepting my limitations is hard – just tonight trying to get my jaw to chew the way I want it to can be hard – it felt like I was chewing three marshmellows or I am just dropping things all the time. My body is changing with the steroids – not for the better! I think the hardest part is I am working hard to maintain what I have – the chance of significant improvement is not great – so unlike most illnesses you where the goal is to get well – here the goal is not to go downhill. (Know as I have said before you have to dance between the miracle and reality)

So all to say life is getting into more of a routine – but definitely not norma!

My spirit is strong, hopeful, thankful the many, many gifts of love, prayers, and support – my energy is strong and I am glad for treatment that is attacking the tumor.

October 5

NANCY'S JOURNAL

In Seattle with Greg. We had a wonderful evening – so quiet – no phone, no interruptions, and dinner delivered by a friend. Everyone wants to come over, be with us. I feel guilty shutting people out but I just cannot interact at the level that would require and be with Greg, as I want to. I want to integrate all but it's way too much. Mostly, I am afraid that people will all disappear and not be here when I need them if I push them away. But there is not enough of me to go around. Clara needs me, Emma needs me, Lilly needs me. I want to be with Greg all that I can and I also desperately need quiet. Greg needs so much activity and it feels like there are people everywhere in our world.

Today Greg is almost normal – enthusiastic, sweet, full of dreams and wanting to help everyone he can. But then there are his limitations: his hand, his face, his speech and sometimes his not making complete sense. There is a way he seems desperate to connect with people and be known. I think I operate much differently.

October 7

NANCY'S CARINGBRIDGE LETTER

Week two of treatment and the world of paradoxes. Greg and I went to Seattle, spent one night and came back the following afternoon. A wonderful "mini-vacation," if you can call radiation and a neuro-oncologist appointment a vacation. It was so nice to be alone together without projects beckoning or the phone ringing. We had a nap, walked on the UW campus and after dinner watched a movie. Such normal activities are a welcome respite.

The daily treatment is going fine. For radiation, Greg is pinned to the table with a mesh mask while the monster machine delivers its killing rays. The daily chemo tablets seem to have no unpleasant side effects.

Staying in Seattle is easier in some ways but coming home to our island for the afternoon is wonderful. Probably the combination of Seattle and our island, as we are doing, is best– but we would really rather not be doing this at all.

It could be said that we are both getting used to the idea that Greg has a malignant brain tumor. Then again it is still a shock. It feels so heavy at times and yet we can still have fun. Sometimes more fun than ever.

Clara's journey is difficult. She yearns to just be a normal fifteen year-old and then she lives in a world at school where her Dad is sorely missed and where she feels such a mixture of complicated feelings all day. Even though all of her friends work to understand, how can they, really? It is a heavy load for her.

While Greg enjoys a lot of social interaction and is on the phone making plans and connecting, I need more space to be alone or with family. I feel badly that I can't communicate regularly or get the simplest things done sometimes.

Timing is everything and I can't predict how I am going to feel from one moment to the next so I ask for understanding. I am pulled strongly in many different directions right now: Greg and the rest of our family, financial planning, tracking all the appointments and medical needs, household stuff, lots of visitors etc. I am also scheduling good things for myself such as Reiki, massage, yoga and my daily walks.

The sunrise these last two days has been exquisite, rising over the layer of fog that lies over the pastures. There are those delicate autumn spider webs gracing the blackberry and rose bushes. They are only visible in the morning when the sun is rising and catches the droplets of moisture. These moments take my breath away. I am grateful for each of them.

October 12

GREG'S CARINGBRIDGE LETTER

The past six weeks seem like a lifetime – we have gathered information, almost a quarter of the way through the chemotherapy/ radiation phase and then we will start some naturalpathic treatments. I enter this week with great hope as the treatments are going well, my medical team is very positive about how my body is responding – what they don't realize is with all your prayers, thoughts, hopes, and energy coming my way the radiation and chemotherapy is just adjunct treatment!

I am feeling good, slightly tired, and finding the back and forth doable but not relaxing! This week I am staying in Seattle three nights to get more rest and work with the biggest challenge – medicines and sleep.

Trying to get quality sleep on steroids is tough, then you add sleeping pills plus a head cold coming on!

I am looking forward to the visit from my English friend Cipri and my sister Jane and her son Christopher this weekend! Anybody that has a hankering for ping pong either come and play or watch this Sunday from

1 – 4 pm – players come sign up at 12:00 and the tables will be up to practice on! This is a benefit for the our island School Trip to Nicaragua next February.

At some point today I was contemplating teaching again – then reality hit. I could not talk all day without totally exhausting my energy because it is hard to form words sometimes or I will not be able to pronounce something. Also without a full functioning left hand there would be many things I could not do. With this tumor I realize how insensitive I have been to people with some sort of disability – I never realized what a struggle each day must be for many people including my students that have those subtle disabilities that we now try to label. I am constantly running up against what I can't do – it is very frustrating to day the least!

I honor those that have deal with a body that is not fully functional.

Peaceful and quiet tonight – hopefully 4:00 am will not find me awake!

October 13

NANCY'S JOURNAL

Last night I had this dream: I was looking for a place for a getaway. I looked both directions and saw green grass and rolling hills both ways. I could go either way; both were appealing. I chose and was looking for a house to stay in. I found one unfinished with tools and gear everywhere and several floors. As I explored, I wondered why it was not finished. I saw a rental agency next door and I wondered if I might ask them if they had a different house to rent. But I remembered that I had to go home for Clara, so I could not spend the night anyway.

October 13

GREG'S CARINGBRIDGE LETTER

Life brings you gifts all the time if you are open to it! So I goto my favorite breakfast cafe on Boat Street – The Offshore Cafe – still serving a huge plate of real hashbrowns , two poached eggs, toast, and coffee bottomless cup) for $5.45!

Anyway their are number of regulars daily and one of them is Bobby – suffers from severe palsy of some kind. He always takes his place at the counter across from the cook and they have an animated conversation with arms, potatoes, and eggs flying around. Then another man walk up says, "how are you doing Bobby?" – for all to hear. Then they engage in a conversation about soccer and I know it is taking everything Bobby can do to communicate.

A delightful addition to the story is the man that sat next to Bobby had a tee shirt that "The 2 1/2 Happy Barbers Shop – Ballard"

Great scene to walk into!

By the way I did some of the best sleep last night I have had!

Good morning at 7:30 am finally!

October 14

NANCY'S JOURNAL

Now all of a sudden it seems like Greg is not really "sick" anymore. He feels good and is doing well so it makes me feel like the tumor has gone away, which is strange because "it" has not gone away. Perhaps our way of approaching it will be changing?

I am aware that as I have more time and am not as needed, I have to re-define myself again. What will I do?

What is important to ME?

October 20

GREG'S CARINGBRIDGE LETTER

A quick update and just to say I thought I was going to have more time to visit people and accomplish some needed projects in my life. However, it seems the daily radiation shot at 10:15am eats up my life with the nearly 8 hour turn around if I come back to the island or just being disoriented and away from Nancy and Clara if I stay in Seattle. This week I made a date to see Clara!

The treatment is going very well – no side effects except being tired and having to take at least one nap a day. I have started to lose my hair which was hard emotionally – the realization that I do have cancer and look like a cancer patient. So I shaved my head again rather than have the patchy look. The poor cat – I almost strangled Smokey because I thought the hairs on my pillow were cat hairs – but of course they were mine!

I had a wonderful week with my friend Cipri (from England) and my *sister, Jane plus nephew Christopher here – and we had a successful table tennis tourney raising over $1000 for the 2011 Nicaragua trip!*

Today was tough – the weight of the tumor, though probably only a few grams, felt big and heavy. Sometimes it is hard to keep up the battle emotionally – I just want it to go away without having the daily grind of being pinned down to a table in a high tech room being shot with radiation. I am blessed with a great team of techs, fast and efficient, and very personal but it is still a hospital, an oncology department, where we are fighting for our lives.

Life can be so good and so bad at the same time.

I do look forward to November 17th – the last day of treatment when I can have my life back and be able to visit some of you!

October 22

NANCY'S CARINGBRIDGE LETTER

It has been a busy couple of weeks but Greg has felt so good that it is almost as if this whole mess is a hoax. In the little world of my mind, I've thought, "maybe they made a mistake," It is only momentary and there are plenty of reminders to bring me back to reality. It is an indication, however, of how well Greg has felt and how well he is doing with his treatment.

It is a gift to have this time, especially because I don't think either of us expected Greg to feel as good as he has felt. With visits from friends and family, we have gathered in all of the good love, laughter and pure fun.

But the daily grind and reality takes its toll. For me, it remains a tornado of confused feelings and questions: Should I have taken a leave from my job? Should I go back? Should I cancel the meals? Shouldn't all of this help be going to others who need it more? Will Greg be alive for _____ or _____? Will my world come crashing in around me tomorrow? Am I crazy to feel good now? Am I crazy to feel bad now? How should I feel?

Then there is the host of "if onlies." I really and truly thought the other day, "If only I could have not turned sixty and had that nice party then everything that happened the next day could not have happened." "If only we could have not gone to Mt. Rainier, then we would not have had to go to the hospital." "If only Seattle did not exist, then we wouldn't have been able to go to the hospital there."

It is amazing how the mind tries to process the incomprehensible.

Tuesday night, when I was feeling good, I read an email that a high school friend had died after undergoing the same treatment that Greg is having for a brain tumor. It set me back a bit.

As I took Cip to the airport on Wednesday I found myself driving by Virginia Mason Hospital and the familiar routes I walked during those nightmare days only two months ago. It shook me deeply. I was rattled by watching Greg and Cip say goodbye and having reminders creep in. It was the saddest day we have had in a while.

Greg and I had some time to cry together that day and it felt good. We took a long walk in the Arboretum and sat in the sun before we went out to dinner! An unusual treat for us.

We got home from Seattle yesterday and after napping in the car, Greg went out and mowed the lawn and raked it before dinner! Go figure, the guy is amazing! It's no wonder I am confused!

I try to look to the future enough to be practical but there is no view of the future to have. I always loved anticipating something fun to plan, adventures to have. It was my way of getting through sometimes-mundane daily life. Now that has all abruptly changed and it is so odd to have no view of the future.

I am deeply grateful to be with Greg each day. It is profound and it scares me sometimes to love this deeply. This is where faith is the only way to keep going. We have been brought so far and we will continue to be led in love into whatever that future holds.

Most people, when they leave home, lock up for fear of break-ins and theft. We don't really have proper locks, thank heavens. We came home to paper hearts on little sticks lining our walkway up to the house and more hearts taped up all over our house inside.

It is times like these that rather than wonder why this awful tumor invaded our lives, that I wonder how we are so fortunate to be this loved and honored? I think of the many, many humans on this planet who suffer alone. I wonder, why us, to be so taken care of?

October 24

NANCY'S JOURNAL

As I went to sleep last night, I tried to imagine Greg being sicker and what it would be like. I really tried to picture the details. I am not sure why—maybe I feel like I need to be in that picture and see who I would be?

It was harder than I thought. Maybe because greater sickness is not as far away as I always thought it would be? In my visualization, I was trying to figure out where to put a hospital bed and then bargaining in my mind that maybe he could just have a pretty, clean antiseptic death in our own bed.

That didn't seem possible. So then I thought about space to put in a hospital bed. It is creepy to imagine him needing mouth sponges and Depends. It all seems horrible and awful and then I thought of his being somewhere else? Unimaginable—he has to be home.

He seems well most of the time but then will have a little break-down and it kills me inside to think of how much he holds together, coping. I know this fucking tumor will get him in the end, but it is hard to believe now. Amazing how I can get used to the limitations and feel grateful that it is only "those things" that are wrong and everything else is ok.

I also thought through if the tumor comes back (and I am assuming it will) and we have to try different drugs, maybe with more side effects, making him sicker – and then what? And for what? God, these may be the decisions we will be making and this is just playtime.

I can go to the place in my mind of seeing myself alone – a widow. I can see that and I hate it and dread it and I am afraid of the grief. What I can't see is this other phase – how long and how complicated will it be? How many decisions will we have to make? The worst thought is what will unfold if we can't keep him at home.

CHAPTER 4

NOVEMBER 2010

where more and more the message is not to
measure anything

—Tony Hoagland, "Into the Mystery"

November 1

NANCY'S CARINGBRIDGE LETTER

Just home from a twelve-hour Monday to-and-from Seattle. We drove down in the pouring rain. Glad to be home safely by the fire tonight.

Today we had a real lift when we met with the doctor and heard that Greg only has eight more treatments! We had thought he had thirteen so this is a gift of a whole extra week of not commuting for us! We will be done with the daily radiology on November 11th.

Our radiation oncologist is positive about Greg's progress. Whenever we talk to him, we go away feeling more confident and optimistic about the future, which makes for a good day.

Over the weekend on our island we had a nice visit with Greg's sister Cathy and niece Lauren. It was a treat and they left feeling impressed with the richness of our community and how well taken care of we are on all levels. Shortly after their arrival, a three-course dinner arrived. Then they were able to get up in a small plane and see our island by air, and Saturday night at dusk we walked a candle lit labyrinth in honor of those souls who have come and gone before us. Our nurturing community shone for them as it does for us every day.

Although it is true we are feeling optimistic, Greg is more tired now, which is to be expected. The wonder steroid drug is helping with the brain swelling while sleeping meds help him sleep. Not exactly what either of us would have chosen but it seems to be working. Our home projects are getting done and hopefully this weekend we can focus here, finish up and encourage the guy to rest a bit.

I am feeling more like myself again. The shock seems to have worn off and I even catch myself thinking toward the future with a smile on my face. I know it could all change in a heartbeat but there can be some great days ahead.

There are losses and sometimes they just jump out right in front of me, sobering. I am willing to live with those losses. What seemed extremely grim a month ago looks much brighter now.

Words fail and many trite expressions of wisdom sound fresh to me: gratitude for each day, love conquering all, breathing through the fears, having faith and courage. It all means so much to me now.

November 9

NANCY'S CARINGBRIDGE LETTER

Only three more days of radiation. I can't believe we have made it through seven weeks of five days a week taking the 6:40 am ferry or spending the night in Seattle. It has been a push and we are sure thankful that it is almost over. Greg is happy to have his life back again. For more of a report, he will have to speak for himself.

As for me, life is a roller coaster. Greg feels well and certainly is not "sick." He is involved in projects, meeting up with people, bringing in firewood, optimistic, attentive. These things are normal.

I have been pondering how I will creatively spend my time since Greg no longer needs much caregiving. A part of me that really thinks, "What was the big deal anyway?" But then the brakes screech and a flood of fears and questions come rushing in. I had one of those paralyzing days today.

I was on the verge of tears all morning for no "real" reason. I took a walk and was enjoying it, listening to music and suddenly my geriatric dog stopped suddenly in front of me and I crashed over him and slid on both knees, hands and one elbow. I might have ended up laughing at the ridiculousness of this kind of thing but not today. I burst into tears, yelled expletives at the dog and at my life. I cried all the way home. I don't want this. I just want a normal life where I come home from work and gripe about being too tired to cook dinner. I want to be able to fantasize about the future. I don't want to be afraid for my children and the losses they might bear. I don't want the weight of the world.

Greg feels good which helps my outlook. He has an amazing

resilience. There is no reason not to feel optimistic. We hear stories all the time about another long-term glioblastoma survivor. Yet there are real losses to feel and grieve. Today was my day to grieve. It is a complicated process. But for now, the evening is quiet.

November 13

GREG'S CARINGBRIDGE LETTER

Freedom... After six and1/2 weeks of Monday through Fridays I am free- free to have more choice in my life. Of course the connection with the medical world is ongoing with at this point probably one appointment a week. The next step is alternative treatment and chemotherapy five days month for six months and then reevaluate. But I am feeling good and looking forward to the days ahead which includes our family reunion at Thanksgiving and a family trip in December followed by our girls favorite holiday- Christmas. So much to be thankful for which includes all the love and support from people on our island and beyond. I cannot but feel in spite of the wars, congressional battles, lack of empathy in this world that people deep in their hearts have the potential to create a world of peace and love.

Of course the paradox I am here in Oregon State University watching, listening to a mass group of young people that have (freshmen) been given total freedom to do whatever they want with I am sure varying degrees of success. The beer companies appreciate our countries method of sending our young people to college after being restricted for years! Lilly, without knowing too many details, is very happy, delighting in showing us " her" world which will include Dad wearing his orange and black t-shirt to the football game today and then going to a toga party at a fraternity with Lilly's sorority sisters. I hope they don't kick old hippies out!

We end with a brunch at Kappa Kappa Gamma on Sunday morning.

So this next phase to me really the stage of mystery – where I am going to turn myself over to the mystery of universe, the power of the grizzly spirit go where I need to go.

November 13

NANCY'S JOURNAL

We arc in Corvallis for Dad's weekend. I spent all day alone. Greg and Lilly are together. I walked in the rain and loved it…I was carefree and wet. There was nothing I had to do, no one to report to – just walking and walking and thinking about my life, other's lives. It is all so strange to look at the date and try to comprehend the last few months. What does it mean? I just can't quite comprehend facing Greg's death and being in the now when he is so strong.

How do we define our lives now? How much are my decisions intertwined with Greg's? Do I make plans for just me? What would those plans be? If we spend time separately, will I regret spending time away from him? I am no longer in crisis mode so now what? How does one live with someone who could die from this tumor but no one knows when? How much of life can be focused on that dying part when it might not happen for a while? But how much can be focused on the living part when it could be ripped away any minute? I could write a book of questions and worries.

November 19

NANCY'S JOURNAL

Such a sad day. It is the first time I have felt so sad and not told Greg. It doesn't seem fair to him.

I feel like I have no one to fall back on. I feel like my rock is crumbling. I miss my strong tall tree. I love my gnarled, kind of broken tree.

I am just so sad and I feel so alone. So much happens, people are busy with their lives. More tragedies occur. We are just one story among many now. It is hard to feel the pain of others now, when mine is so big.

Chapter 5

December 2010

to love life, to love it even
when you have no stomach for it
and everything you've held dear
crumbles like burnt paper in your hands

—Ellen Bass, "The Thing Is"

December 2

Nancy's Journal

Such a sad day. We went to the Oncologist and it was more of the same information but somehow it hit really hard. For Greg, it was all that he hoped would not be true and it was more than he could take. He cried and cried.

It is so easy to say, "Oh the doctors don't know, you can be the exception," but truthfully, the doctors do know and there is a reality here that is hard to avoid. I feel less hopeful about the future than Greg does but I am willing to be wrong. I have not been thinking about the harsh realities for a while and now I don't know how to feel.

I go out with friends and I feel like I have a black cloud hanging over my life. I am so very tired: tired from all of the company, and worried about my children. I don't feel like I am fulfilling my responsibility as a parent.

December 6

NANCY'S JOURNAL

It is snowing and beautiful. Clara and her friends are outside in the snow and having great fun. It makes me feel happy to see their joy and yet I feel so much grief at the same time.

December 7

NANCY'S CARINGBRIDGE LETTER

Life has been full with those we love from near and far, and full with a wide array of emotion. We had a good post-treatment week with preparation for Thanksgiving. Then, with a blast of cold wind (literally), the family arrived.

We settled into a couple of houses, played many games of octuplet solitaire (a vicious Ewert family game sometimes resulting in injury), and woke up on Thanksgiving morning to a landscape covered in beautiful snow. We had walks on our precious island and our warm community showed itself off to all of the Ewert clan. We shared food and laughter and wonderful, focused appreciation circles for Greg and for each other.

We are grateful to have such a loving, supportive family and this special Thanksgiving time together. We acknowledged the fragility of life we share together and are the richer for it.

Greg and I continue to live with the harsh reality of this wicked tumor. It is the black cloud that hangs over our lives. Thankfully, it seems to recede at times, but, sadly, it never really goes away. It hits us all in different ways at different times and then we go on. These are difficult days. Maybe we are in a new phase of realization? Whatever it is, Greg and I are actively grieving our enormous loss.

He is more tired and weaning off the steroids that contribute to fatigue. The good news is that he is sleeping more and this blessed sleep comes easily. But he does not have energy. We are never sure what all of this means. Will he continue to have more symptoms now and not rebound as he has in the past, or is this just the expected fatigue from the effects of radiation and chemo?

From a recent MRI, we know that the tumor has shrunk, but there is a question about some other spots. They could be parts of the disintegrating tumor or could be new smaller tumors. It is all speculation at this point and we must live with uncertainty and wait for the next MRI in late February.

Greg picks himself up and attends to home and school projects in a way that still amazes me. He goes where he is needed and fills so many gaps and hearts, just the way he has. He is willing to help a friend, be the best Dad and husband one could want, and support the kids and the school with all that he has to offer.

Moments of beauty and wonder accompany me on this arduous, bumpy road. I can feel joy and light, even if just for a short time. The winter sun meanders through the trees and lights up the oh-so-green moss on our island Hill. I feel the magnificent winter sunset over the water and the ever-present acts of kindness shown to us.

There seems to be an unending well of kindness and love channeled through the people who grace our lives. Nothing can take away the profound depths of sorrow into which we are obviously asked to dive. In some way I may never be able to explain, the accompaniment of such great love somehow eases the path a little.

Now we wait and watch, pray and hope. We gather our family of five at the end of this week and travel to St. Lucia. We have ten days there together. We are more grateful than we can ever say for all of those who were able to make this happen for us, and all those helping here so we can be gone. I pray that our family can share deeply and take in every moment together.

December 10

GREG'S CARINGBRIDGE LETTER

Nancy filled in beautifully our present state of being along with, as always, her honest feelings. With my limited touch typing skills I will catch up on where this tumor has taken me. Treatment was intense – not in terms of discomfort, but the time and internal fortitude, the walls I had to build and the knowledge I was fighting for my life. This treatment was essential to knock back this beast – at this point it is a beast I am battling! So after 30 treatments, faced pinned down, combined with a nightly cereal bowl of medicines including chemo pills (no telling which bodily function is altered by which pill!), the Seattle runs are done but it seems the ongoing medical appointments will continue (three last week!).

My personal work has been to avoid being sucked into the the time clock I live under of medical prognosis. Last week was tough to stay afloat as we heard news of a possible new small tumor though the main tumor has decreased as expected – combined with more numbness on my left side. Just knowing the beast is waiting in the wings sometimes hits me really hard. Then I paddle hard to bring myself back to the surface, back to face the beast, knowing the longer I stay alive the more time I have with my girls, Nancy , friends, family, and some of my unfulfilled dreams.

The timing of our trip is perfect – a time to just hang together as a family. I feel so blessed to have this time really made possible by the generous community we live in – thank you! Funny the things that help make me feel normal – helping tutor students or yesterday just replacing the front pads on our Toyota – getting grease under my fingernails! Sadly, I am missing our great annual Winter Solstice celebration this year but will dance around the fire in spirit – which in a way is what I am doing on my good weeks to keep the beast in the shadows! Happy holidays – your love, support, and care had help sustain us all through this time.

December 12

NANCY'S JOURNAL

We are here in St. Lucia. It is warm and we have swum in the pool and in the ocean with all five of us riding waves together in the sunset. Such healing. There is much creative force with us now: creating new memories while we love each other and the life we have been given. Off to my mosquito net bed.

December 13

NANCY'S JOURNAL

This is so much like other family vacations that our life seems "normal." I have more confidence in Greg being in charge now and that feels good. Can't this last forever? I didn't feel sad for two days. Occasionally, I would stop and remember the "truth" but not for long. How do I know what the truth is anyway? Maybe the truth is that his tumor is dying and he isn't. God, I hope so. Life is easier in the sun, in another world, with no reminders of all we have been through.

December 16

NANCY'S CARINGBRIDGE LETTER

The sun calls and in just a moment I will be diving into the pool right out my door. The flowers are all colors of orange, yellow, white, coral and fuchsia. Greg is lounging by the pool and is doing so well here enjoying our wonderful family time full of good talks, happy kids, happy adults acting like kids, good food and lovely welcoming people here. It is all we would have wanted and more.

December 19

NANCY'S JOURNAL

It has been a real tumor vacation. I can honestly say that I don't think that much about Greg's tumor here. It feels like "something that happened that changed our lives," but in the past. Maybe he really is better? Maybe the treatment is really shrinking the tumor? We are almost normal here: no one knows all that has happened to us.

A part of me feels sad when I watch Greg just trying to be himself and I wish those who are interacting with him could really know him, know the Greg without the tumor. Do they see him as a little bit "less than?" Maybe not, maybe it is only me who sees glimpses of the loss. It is like an accelerated aging process: my 61 year-old husband is suddenly 70.

CHAPTER 6

JANUARY 2011

What can anyone give you greater than now,
starting here, right in this room, when you turn
around?

—William Stafford, "You Reading This,
Be Ready"

January 7

NANCY'S CARINGBRIDGE LETTER

Our holidays are over. The Christmas decorations are put away and the days are gray and rainy.

St. Lucia was a perfect beginning to the holiday. We had the pure luxury of time to be together and relax, talk, laugh, tell stories and get some new stories. The water was heavenly. On our last day we spent hours just floating together and riding the waves in the rain while singing Christmas carols at the top of our lungs. Greg felt good there. His talent, developed when we lived in England, of driving on the left side of the road while sitting behind a steering wheel on the right side of the car, is still intact. He got us everywhere safely.

We returned to Washington on Solstice night and the next day our whole family geared up, got the tree, made dozens of cookies and a gingerbread house. The girls came up with the idea of going to the village and handing out cookies to everyone we saw. We all five wore our Santa hats on Christmas Eve and had a great time filling the tummies of lovely our islandians.

On Christmas day, Greg and I were presented with a beautiful memory quilt made for us by friends. The girls were involved in the making of it too. It is full of old family photos set in prayer flags. It is exquisitely beautiful and as we looked at it, we all five sat down and cried together—something I think we had needed to do but just had not gotten to yet.

I am amazed and in awe of the wisdom expressed by our children. As we all talked about what is difficult for us and how we cope, they shared their thoughts and feelings articulately and beautifully. Thank God they have each other and that we have them. It is a rich and valued gift.

Greg felt good all through the holidays but this week he is experiencing a downturn. It is hard to see, discouraging for him and scary for all of us. His left hand has more numbness and is not operating well and he is not as nimble on his feet. Talking is more difficult. He is feeling down. The reality of this tumor and the toll it takes is glaring now and it is difficult not to feel overwhelmed by it all.

Despite how he felt all week, Greg still participated in the our island Center for Community and the Arts interviews and did some tutoring at our house. The students were thrilled to spend time with him again. They never knew math could be so fun. That is the Greg we all know and love and that part is still very much alive.

We wait for another MRI in late January. We wonder all the time. It is difficult to keep that fire- breathing dragon of fear and horror from coming into the door and taking over our lives. Mostly right now, I am just profoundly sad. I wake up some mornings and have the sinking feeling that we all get when something awful has occurred, but the balm of sleep has made us forget for a while.

I can speak for the girls and myself to say that we are deeply grateful for Greg every day. I lie in bed and feel the blood pulsing through his veins and say a prayer of gratitude every night for just that.

Emma said yesterday, "I know it is hard for him and I feel so bad about that, but for me it does not matter that he drops things or trips or has lost his hair, he is still my Dad and as long as I have that, as long as I can talk to him, that is what matters."

Has there ever been a dad who is so loved by his children?

January 7

GREG'S CARINGBRIDGE LETTER

A New Year- Glad to finish the last one. It is the shits having a brain tumor. My left hand constantly reminds me that the tumor is there due to numbness and lack of grip as I drop things all of the time. My balance is slightly off so sometimes I trip or stumble. Other times I can feel the pressure of the tumor in my brain. The scariest part for me is with this slight decline in my functioning on the left side, I wonder if this is the beginning of the end. My goal is to keep my body from going downhill knowing that this type of cancer is aggressive and could find a gap in the chemo or my attitude and grow quickly. I don't know how much time I have left or what I can plan for. How much time do I have left with my girls or my wife?

I had to say goodbye to Emma yesterday and I wonder if she will ever see me function as I am today or will it be a phone call to come home and see Dad while he is still coherent? I am tired of this tumor in my head and I want it out. I want it to leave me alone. How do I possibly make peace with it? I am struggling with being tired, especially during the 5 days a month of chemo.

Now we are through the main part of the medical treatment and I am going to focus on writing my story and work on Clara's '57 VW. I am off to see my Dad in Michigan who just finished radiation and chemo for throat cancer and has a clear bill of health at 95.

In spite of the daily grind and all that is not easy, I appreciate all of the love and support that comes my way. It helps keep me going.

January 13

NANCY'S CARINGBRIDGE LETTER

Life here is like living in the car of a roller coaster. Greg went in for his MRI yesterday, which was ahead of schedule because of the increase of symptoms. He also went back on steroids. Today we got the results: first, a call saying that the tumor appears to have grown and that it is likely they will switch him to another drug; second, a call a few hours later saying that what looks like new growth is perhaps more likely to be radiation necrosis.

They will take the MRI to neuro rounds next week and give us more information then. It is so difficult to determine conclusively. We were told several times early in the game that this might happen but still we are human and we crave factual, concrete information.

Today Greg and I decided to go to Hawaii in February. It is the only state he has never been to. I have never been there either and am excited.

January 19

NANCY'S CARINGBRIDGE LETTER

We have talked to the doctors again this week about the MRI and everyone seems to agree that it is most likely radiation necrosis showing and not new tumor growth. This sounds to us like good news but we still wonder about the loss of function in his left hand. Happy to say that the sun came out on our island today. It was heavenly. The lilac is starting to bud as are the blueberries and there is a bit of pink rhubarb starting to sprout! Amazing, as is this moon. Hope it is shining on you all.

January 20

NANCY'S CARINGBRIDGE LETTER

A couple of nights ago I read about Ted Kennedy and news reports about his treatment. He, of course, had access to the best of whatever is out there and it is exactly the same treatment that Greg is having. I feel grateful for the wonderful, concerned medical care Greg has and grateful that we have the health insurance to pay for it.

When this all first happened, we were deluged with articles, ideas, etc. Should we go here? Should we go there? Do we have to leave our home for months to get the "best"? All our medical practitioners have treated us with such respect and compassion. Our phone calls are always returned and we have constant access to our medical team as we need it, even from such a distance. My heart aches for folks who do not have this kind of care.

The signs of spring that I saw yesterday are buried in a chilly wind today, gray skies and rain.

January 27

GREG'S CARINGBRIDGE LETTER

Returned Tuesday from Michigan visiting my 95 year old father who lives by himself in his home in East Lansing. An amazing man — because of his last bout with throat cancer he survives with a feeding tube which he takes care of himself. With siblings in the area to attend to some of the details- medical and daily chores he gets help when he needs it — but he needs very little! We had some nice talks because we are running down not too dissimilar paths in terms of maintaining bodies, meds, elimina-tion problems, and the emotional swings of dealing with our "our disabilities — not being able to do what we were capable of just a short time ago.

Flying back on my own , driving around Michigan, being on my

own was such freedom! After last fall , always needing a

driver I almost felt normal again!

Right now my meds feel very balanced, I am feeling energetic and SO glad to have a couple weeks ahead without major plans (except chemo next week). With brain tumor there is always something " next" — it is just how far!

Nancy and I were in Seattle last night for a brain tumor support group of mostly high functioning tumor patients and spouses.k However one sad story- marathon runner, skier, sports nut about 60, had surgery in December and is now in a wheelchair.

Counting my blessings this morning that I can drive back to our island!

CHAPTER 7

FEBRUARY 2011

Then you hold life like a face . . .
no charming smile, no violet eyes,
and you say, yes, I will take you
I will love you, again.

—Ellen Bass, "The Thing Is"

February 6

NANCY'S JOURNAL

Greg is doing much better than I thought he would be. Our days are peaceful. Greg is working on the VW all of the time. The steroids get him going and he gets very manic. He does not see this at all but he can hear me when I can finally get him to sit down and listen. I cried all day yesterday. *ALL DAY.* Everything made me cry. The garden has rabbits, my back hurts and I can't move dirt. I just cannot imagine living in this house alone. It is terrifying. I can talk about it logically but then all of a sudden the floodgates open and every terror I have ever had comes forth. Some days Greg is so focused on himself and his projects because he feels better— but he forgets about me. Yesterday I felt so lonely for him, almost like he was already gone.

February 8

GREG'S CARINGBRIDGE LETTER

A quick note to say I am in a sweet place right with energy, meds balanced, and getting a chance to tackle honey do lists as well as my own projects. My hair is growing back in patches but it is growing.

Have a great group of guys helping finish my '57 VW restoration for Clara- getting very close to completion – engine went in Saturday.

Life is good – early mornings again with strong energy.

Of course the shitty part is I can always feel exactly where the tumor is lurking in my brain just silently waiting for a time to strike. My next tumor check (MRI) will be mid- March – hoping for a "where did it go ?" report.

Coffee pot is on at 5 a.m.!

February 8

NANCY'S JOURNAL

We tried to make reservations to go to Greece in May and leave Clara with her older sister. She would not rise to the occasion. She wants us here for her prom, her track meets. She says, "I want to be normal, I don't want to have to grow up now," but then she says, "I want you to go, I don't want to hold you back," and she means that, too.

I want to help her have a normal life but how do Greg and I manage what we want and need for ourselves, too? I find myself resenting the girls and their needs for me sometimes because I want time with Greg. They are not dying and he is. What is fair to ask of them? What is too much?

February 8

NANCY'S CARINGBRIDGE LETTER

Greg continues to be frustrated with the lack of functioning in his left hand and sometimes speech articulation is more difficult, but it does not stop him. From my point of view, he has patience way beyond normal and, I swear, double my capacity to accomplish anything in a day. No wonder he was such a good teacher.

Life is better than we ever imagined, really and yet there are still days when *"IT"* smacks one of us in the face full on.

I had one of those days of being smacked on Saturday. Every fear I ever had came back to me with a vengeance and the trauma took over for a while.

If I think for a minute about the future, it is difficult. How will I do "this," how will I ever manage "that"? The house feels overwhelming to me, as does parenting, finding a job, making major life decisions etc. I used to be so independent before I met Greg at age thirty-seven and now I feel like I have lost all of that independence because we live life as a team.

The truth is, today we still have our "team" and I am relishing in that blessing more than ever. We share the profound loss as well as all that is enjoyable.

Clara leaves for her service trip to Nicaragua next week— the trip that Greg started at our high school many years ago. They go every two years with Greg in the lead and this was the year that Clara and I would finally get to join him. Now she is going without either of us. It is sad for all of us. It is a life changing experience; we both wish we could be sharing it with her.

February 14

NANCY'S CARINGBRIDGE LETTER

I have been thinking a lot about love today since it is Valentine's Day. Our family has been the recipient of more love in the last six months than we ever imagined existed and it fills me with surprise and wonder.

I am taken back to the moment in the ER when we first heard the words "glioblastoma." I closed my eyes and prayed at that moment. I prayed for us to be held and guided and to find our way. It was surely the most fervent prayer of my life.

Never did I imagine that so much of "finding our way" would mean the outpouring of love that began on that day and continues. Love shown in words, meals, gardening, clean windows, an incredible scrapbook, financial help, miles for traveling, visits from many and guest accommodations to help them, books, words, hours spent taking Greg to Seattle, shared tears, work on the part of many in our house, personal organizers, the VW, and so much more. We have footsteps beside ours literally and figuratively: well-worn paths of love.

Our future is uncertain and scary, but knowing what I have learned during this time about love gives me a faith I never knew before. I know that regardless of how alone I might feel, I will not be alone, ever.

Love has landed and found fertile ground here. There is plenty of water to nourish the growth and there will be sunshine too.

February 14

GREG'S CARINGBRIDGE LETTER

Brain tumor reality 101.

It is so different for each person ... Location,location , location.... Even though all the houses are scheduled for demolition some are better than others to live in! Right now I am grateful for my assigned home, I can talk clearly most of the, time, my left side of my body (legs/arms) is about 30 percent weaker,swallowing can be like eating jet puff marshmellows sometimes, it takes about ten minutes to button a shirt, I get tired from the tumor and the meds so naps are nice and necessary, I drop things that are in my left hand, sometimes lose my balance, and my glasses — those are all part of my " new" normal. Accepting this has been challenging yet how grateful I am that speech is only somewhat affected and I still can walk (7 miles at the ocean), and at least at this time I am to do most of what I want to do! I also very complete almost all parts of my life. My happy meter is high these days.

What I want to honor and speak to this morning is three wonderful girls and my dear wife. .. They too are experiencing brain cancer 101(maybe it is a grad course by now!) and it is difficult at best. Each of my dear daughters are handling this in a way helping them cope with the potential loss of their "Dad"- all have had to look at life with new lenses. In Lilly's Christmas poster she wants me to walk her down the isle. Clara is on the island and can not escape the reality as easily as Emma and Lilly. And how can young friends in high school know how to support a young person that has deep moments of sorrow. For me a recent theme has been what will be my unfulfilled dreams — most of them center around what I will miss with Nancy, my girls and grand children. I want to be there in full body and soul, I want to touch and love them all — when is one ever complete with that?

So my family , not only has pulled together in a sweet love nest but we recognize and feel the pain daily as well – though I don't want to hear sometimes I hear again , sitting in Group Health- "It is a tumor". Clara ,Nancy, and I burst into puddle of tears! Since that time we are learning to cope the best we can, each on our own path and on the path together. I am so thankful for Nancy's ability to express her thoughts in writing and handling all the scheduling, medical communication, and the myriad of details that we have had to deal with since last August 20th as well as being super mom to our lovely girls.

Through this our family has grown larger that includes many of you as you follow our journey – please continue to hold my girls and Nancy in your hearts as we continue walking down this path.

February 16

NANCY'S JOURNAL

A dream – Greg and I were in a boat at a dock. I was walking from one end to the other and I lost my balance and fell into the water. I knew I could have caught myself, but I also knew that falling would be ok. He was worried and upset but I knew I was fine. I loved the feeling of falling deep into the water and I knew I would re-emerge and tell him I was ok.

February 17

NANCY'S JOURNAL

Hard day...I was out of sorts, losing things. Greg had a hard day too. He was yelling tonight with frustration. He couldn't swallow and it was scary. I insisted that he take more sleep meds because he does not sleep. It feels like he is slipping and I am scared. Nervous about traveling with him. Will this trip be our last?

February 25

NANCY'S JOURNAL

Up at 5 am, can't sleep. Last night Greg told me that his head felt "weird", like he can feel something in his head. I just wanted to scream, "Don't tell me that!" When other people are around, even the girls, he acts like all is well but as soon as it is just us, things are not well. I am not as good at cheering him up or providing the distraction that others can provide. Sometimes though things are still normal. When we talk about plans for the near future, I don't question that things will be any different than they are today. But after watching him yesterday, I can feel how quickly it can all crumble.

The girls were having a silly discussion about which one of them I would live with when I get older. Then I realized that we think about the long-term future without Greg in it. He is not a part of the future in any of our minds because we know he won't be there—but then he is here now. It is so much to try making sense of.

February 27

GREG'S CARINGBRIDGE LETTER

Hawaii! Just walked up from the beach on Molokai, stars out, gentle waves coming from the west – peaceful, soothing, a paradise I did not know about! I started traveling late in my life so what I have seen is limited but this is a place that speaks to me. We had two hour layover in Honolulu – and the jumped on a smaller plane to Molokai. Just getting out of the plane and having a warm breeze filled with sweet smells was healing. (Especially after leaving Seattle's 20 degrees and on top of that I got in my first car accident in my life near our hotel – police, fire engine the whole nine yards – we are fine and the car is drivable though the right rear panel of our Toyota is not!)

Back to Molokai – from the airport we drive to the "largest" town on the island – one main street, small grocery store, sweet and pricey (milk $8.00a quart!) and the drive to the west end where our condo is waiting about 25 miles away. I don't think it was a deja vu experience for me but the landscape we drove through felt so comforting to me – it felt "right" and I am sure some people would simply say "why am I here?". I described it as desolate but only because there were no signs of human habitation (my definition of a fine place!) yet the colors of the small rolling hills and valleys were exquisite – brown, purplish earth with bright green shrubs all enhanced by the setting sun peeking through dark clouds. The patches of colors almost looked like those paint by numbed oil paintings I got as a kid for Christmas only so much more alive. The visual was only made more vivid with a strong, delicate, earthy breeze blowing over my tumor zone. (My hair is growing back in patches!) for whatever reason this place feels RIGHT – as did James Island when I discovered the San Juans. However, I am finding warm , balmy thick, air to be very delightful and healing....

The timing of this trip is perfect – first it is the longest trip Nancy and I have since B.C. (before children) and the last week I struggled with feeling shifts in my body – more numbness on the left side, face getting puffy from steroids (looking in the mirror and seeing someone else, a cancer patient), much more tired than I had been for a month, and variety *of little indicators of change and the kind of changes I do not want! I am just getting to a point where I accepting what I do have with my "new normal".*

So this morning I sit in this open air lovely condo, listening to the waves, feeling like I have found a "peace" of heaven ...grateful for the many gifts in my life, grateful all of you that are sharing this journey with us.

CHAPTER 8

MARCH 2011

*I pause in this moment at the beginning of my old age
and I say a prayer of gratitude for getting to this
evening*

*a prayer for being here, today, now, alive
in this life, in this evening, under this sky.*

—David Budbill, "Winter: Tonight: Sunset"

March 1

NANCY'S CARINGBRIDGE LETTER

It is too beautiful here to describe. The waves are powerful and ever so beautiful.

We had another wonderful day of exploring and relaxing. I read my book on the beach and swam laps again while Greg read, napped and lounged on the beach, exhausted after the stress of emptying the garbage!

Tomorrow we get up early and go out on a boat to see Humpback whales.

March 1

LILLY'S CARINGBRIDGE LETTER

I just wanted to write a quick note to say thank you so much to everyone for supporting my family and giving my parents the opportunity to go to Hawaii. I just got off the phone with them and started crying out of happiness because they are so at peace, joyful and my dad is feeling better then he has in weeks. Thank you so much!

March 5

GREG'S CARINGBRIDGE LETTER

If holidays are supposed to be a relaxing escape this was the best for me – for us. I let my body dictate when I would rest, go to the beach, or when we go on an outing. I got up at odd hours, went to sleep early and in general pampered myself. We cooked together (though I followed the head chef's directions!), ate fresh vegetables from a local farm that included fresh mango and papaya, and gathered with the local condo owners at the beach for the sunset.

All to say I feel better than I have for a long time. Back to reality on Saturday – very excited to hear the returning Nicaragua student's and Clara's stories of their adventure south – needless to say a very different warm air "holiday"!

After a week like this – the exquisite blue-green water, the sun blazing into my tumor burning it out, floating in the ocean, hills of purple and deep red earth nurturing bright, bright green, shrubs glowing in the sun – it makes staying alive as long as I can the best option! I can tell you how odd it sometimes to be SO far way from having a tumor and the you get a grim reminder (you cannot button a shirt, my left hand becomes numb, I have trouble getting words out or I cannot swallow my pills –

In spite of the weather on our island, I look forward to being home, a place of comfort, friends, support, and love.

March 8

NANCY'S CARINGBRIDGE LETTER

Leaving Molokai

I sat on the soft white sand beach close to our condo yesterday mesmerized by the power of the waves as they crashed into shore. Here they really crash. I walked back to the condo and looked at the vivid colors of the flowers and was brought to tears at the beauty of life and the fragility that we face with Greg's prognosis. It has been a time of grace for us here in Hawaii. We have dreamed for years of going to a warm, tropical place, just the two of us. And here it is– a brain tumor that led us here.

Why do the heaviness and our fears of the future dissipate in the sun? I do not know, but they do. We had fun drives listening to Hawaiian reggae and laughed and sang together. "Tumor life" was a million miles away.

Now we go home to our wonderful friends, dogs, cat, Clara and a week of chemo. More responsibilities call.

Aloha for now...

March 18

NANCY'S JOURNAL

What a strange peace our lives are in nowadays. It feels like this peace will never end. We are all content with each other and I feel a stability that does not make sense when I realize that our world is completely upside down compared to this time last year. We have lost so much: dreams of the future, vitality, security, but in some ways we have gained so much. We don't have time for petty disagreements. Planning for the "future" is no longer a burden in any way because we simply can't. Am I crazy to feel so carefree? I think maybe, but I like being a little crazy.

March 21

NANCY'S CARINGBRIDGE LETTER

It feels like years ago that we were in Hawaii. Coming home was improved greatly by getting to hear story after story from Clara's trip to Nicaragua. They had a rich experience, working hard, supporting each other and learning about the struggles of debilitating poverty. Clara is following in the photography footsteps of her father we had the feeling we had been there, after her photos and stories.

The group took the spirit of Greg with them. Many of the workers remember him fondly from his past trips and sent along those memories and well wishes with Clara.

I was only home for a few days and took off for Montreal to see Emma in college. It makes such a difference to physically be in someone's space and life. Emma has done so well navigating a huge school and international city. She finishes the year at the end of April and has one more semester next fall.

It's such a time of transition for young people with a whole life ahead and a world of choices. I am mystified at how we all found our way. Emma is just hoping that Greg's health holds out long enough to finish in the fall. My heart aches for her to be so far away. She has good friends but no one can really understand what it is like to have a parent with a terminal illness and all of the uncertainty that it involves.

In some ways, it is a gift for her to have another life to be absorbed into–but then the knowledge of "what is really happening" creeps in uninvited and painful. I got a taste of what it is like to be away and only have the phone to get a glimpse into how Greg is doing daily. I realize that this is what she has had to grapple with all year.

She and I had some very tender moments. I held my sweet twenty-two-year-old baby while she cried and talked of her fears and questioning of how to navigate her near future with this big uncertainty that no one can adequately advise her about. As hard as it is, I am grateful that our family has been given this time to process all of this in all our different ways.

While we were in Hawaii, Greg's father began to have significant health problems and was hospitalized. He ended up being transferred to an inpatient Hospice facility last week and died peacefully on Saturday night with family around him. Greg is grateful that he had the time with his Dad in January. We are all going to Michigan tomorrow.

Overall, Greg is doing well and holding his own. His zest for life and love of his projects is hardly diminished. We continue to work with the medication challenges. His next MRI is April 4th and it is nerve-wracking to wonder what it will show. Daffodils are blooming on our island and the weeping willow has baby green tiny leaves.

March 21

Greg's CaringBridge Letter

My Father passed the night before last. He was 95 years old.

Dad's life spanned nearly a hundred years of amazing changes in our world! Born in 1915 he saw planes develop from flimsy flying machines to supersonic jet travel; Tin Lizzies to formula race cars; telephones which needed an operator to I-phones; a world based in small towns and individual stores to massive marketing by chain stores and a country ruled by corporations, typewriters to high speed computers, from a world relative free from human impact to a serious global warming crisis, from a world of 1.8 billion people to almost 7 billion people ...my Father saw and lived through probably the most dramatic 100 years in history – and that included two World Wars!

My Dad, Quentin, grew up in a small town, Grand Ledge, MIchigan, during the depression. HIs father, Albert, was the beloved Episcopal minister in town, which meant that money was scarce. Dad worked hard to help the family and eventually through years of schooling became a well respected lawyer, I think partially to make sure he could provide for a family without a financial struggle and he did! He had a family of five children, a wife, Frances, dogs, the whole nine yards.

My relationship with my father was strained at times, especially during the 60's when I came home from the West Coast with long hair and a peace symbol around my neck – a conservative mid -West lawyer had trouble understanding my politics and my dress code ... but like many of us during that era time does heal and Dad and learned to acknowledge and accept our differences. His philosophy was "the older you get the more conservative you get" – oh well!

What my Father gave me that was essential to who I am now was a safety net – I always knew that I had financial and emotional support I needed and that allowed me freedom to explore who I was and what I wanted to be. I thank him for that. As a result I was able to find my passion, teaching, and made a career of it.

I watched him approach his death carefully – when his quality of life went downhill dramatically the past couple of weeks (he had been on a feeding tube for six months and the was on oxygen the last couple of weeks) he choose to go into hospice and transition to another world. Such irony that only six months ago I was walking my father down the hall to receive radiation treatment for tongue cancer the one month later I was being strapped to a table for after being diagnosed brain cancer.

I said my goodbye to him in January when I went back to Michigan and I think, really, he hoped he would go before me – we never want to lose our children.

He died peacefully , surrounded by family ... I was told he took three big breaths and then moved on. He is an inspiration to me in how to negotiate that path ... how does one walk gracefully to death? I just have to trust I can do that.

As I said to Dad, who at one point in his life, enjoyed a martini or two, ... save at place at the bar for me – I will see you sometime ... hopefully not for a few years!

March 21

NANCY'S JOURNAL

Greg's Dad died last night. The true patriarch, so now we will go to Michigan – another crazy upheaval. Upheavals seem normal now. Greg is at peace with it but it carries some weight for sure. He shed some tears and it brought up plenty of questions for him about how he will go. The whole concept seems so foreign to both of us. The fact that he will die does not seem real. But living with the tumor is real – the steroids, the big belly, the puffy cheeks, the speech problems.

So many problems.

Mostly Greg is feeling resilient but tonight was a bad night. He hates this tumor so much. He went to bed sad, frustrated and angry... and afraid. He is afraid of the next MRI. How can it be bad when he is doing so well? It just has to show no tumor growth, it has to.

CHAPTER 9

APRIL 2011

*. . . There never was
anything else. Only these excruciatingly
insignificant creatures we love.*

—Ellen Bass, "The Big Picture"

April 1

NANCY'S JOURNAL

Greg is Mr. Energy today as usual. He goes in spurts and then crashes. He does so much for others. I feel a lack of purpose for myself, like I am not really doing anything for anyone else. I try to read the news so I have a sense of what is going on in the world but I don't' quite get there. I can't really concentrate on any of it.

I have this feeling that if I put my energy into anything else besides Greg and our family, it might get taken away. I just don't have energy for world problems right now and it makes me feel really guilty. I gave myself a year last August when Greg was first diagnosed to stay focused here. I am still in "my year" but sometimes my life feels so small.

I know I am also "saving up" energy for what is to come, like putting money in the bank. But I don't know what is to come?

The MRI is Monday and everything in life hinges on it. Greg is scared and feels like he is racing against a clock.

He tells me today that he is going to lead a sailing trip with kids this summer. It sounds *crazy* to me but I know that is what keeps him going.

Terror lurking just below the surface of calm…

April 4

NANCY'S JOURNAL

I feel like the whole world is waiting for Greg's MRI results…so many calls and emails. It is all well intended but, quite honestly, overwhelming for me since it feels like our whole life is on the line.

All of this attention from others outside of our family takes energy *out* of me when I need every bit of that energy to focus *in* to calm myself and process. It takes so much out of me to feel other's anxiety, even though I know they care.

I am trying to find an anchor now: something to keep me steady and secure. I am not sure there is one. This is a *very* scary time. How many times and ways can I say that over and over?

April 5

GREG'S CARINGBRIDGE LETTER

I had my MRIi yesterday morning so we are hoping to get the results this afternoon–we will post what we know. After this 4 month time post radiation they should be able to give us a better sense of what has happened to the tumor since lastMRI three months ago, I am hoping a small or non- existent tumor -thank you for holding your thoughts and prayers with me today.(typing continues to be frustrating in 52 words there were mistakes in over 1/3 of them!)

I an doing okay these days – feeling way too tired and ˆ am moor frustrated with my bodies limit...hard yo accept. nervous and scared today

We just had our phone call from the Doctor and the tumor has shrunk....not a lot but enough for him to say "we are moving in the right direction". We are grateful and relieved.

I think the news for me that the tumor presently is shrinking with our current treatment and that it will give me more quality time is such a relief! though the Dr. can not say for sure but it does look like I get a good summer with my family and friends – and my next MRI in late June will my next benchmark. I Just want as much time I can get! Even though it is hard living with uncertainty it is much better to live!

Thank you for all your thoughts, prayers , and love – that probably does more than the chemo!

A very good day today!

April 7

GREG'S CARINGBRIDGE LETTER

First, thank you for your flood of support I was deeply touched and did not realize how many people are following my story. I truly believe your support, thoughts, and prayers are pounding at the tumor and it does not dare to come out!

I have a story to pass on this morning ... So I am sitting at the computer at 2:30 in the morning eating two eggs (over easy or easy over – I never know which one is right but I always seem to get the same thing with either phase!) of course I did not attempt poached eggs though that's whatI really wanted. BY the way, if you have not gone to the Love Dog Cafe for their weekend breakfast and snatched a couple of poached eggs from the Queen of poached eggs White Bear) – great food ,reasonable prices – under $5 for breakfast and this is not rural Montana!

Oh the story – so Monday I do my head in the tube (MRI) with machine guns going off at regular intervals, Nancy retrieves my next five days of chemo medicine from the pharmacy, stuffs the $3,000 worth of poison in my green string bag and we charge home for the 12: 45 ferry. I get there at 12:36 and of course we misread the new ferry schedule – ferry left at 12:35 just like it should! Has anybody else ever done that?

After finding ways to hang around Anacortes for four hours – car wash, actually time to vacuum the car, library, Marine Hardware back rooms, etc, I make it to the ferry get home and unload.

Eveining comes and i go to get my Chemo and we cannot find it anywhere! You can imagine the search we did – and nothing. The only thing I might have done is throw it in the trash at the car wash thinking it was garbage (it was in a small bag that had been squashed in my string bag – though that would seem unlikely.

Went to bed, tried to sleep, and the next morning I called the Bubble n' Suds – "We have already emptied the trash" – gone! I called good friend at Group Health Pharmacy who would see what she could do and we were informed the the policy is you lose it you pay for it! This is not baby aspirin! Then customer service – sorry .... "I can connect you with your oncologist so he can order more" .... after " push one to speak someone from India, push 7 for your horoscope today, and push 4 for "you are pushing your luck if you want a real human being", (you know the scene!) I was able to talk to Sharon , a nurse, explained the situation, she said, "let me see what I can do". Three minutes later she came back on the line and said, "call the pharmacy – they will replace it – no charge but I will have to pay the shipping!"

Whew!!!!!!!!!!!!!!!!!!!!! A angel!

All to say this world is full of gifts and love. People you don't even know reaching out with a helping hand. The classics random acts of kindness... I will never know what happened behind the scenes

and I am forever grateful.

This brain tumor ride has SO many facets to it with gifts upon gifts of spirit, connections I never would have made, healing in our extended family, Nancy being loved and cared for by my family , my girls growing up quickly having to face losing their Dad, Nancy being our strong emotional pillar trying to find a way to ground herself as we move forward and then just when we get some stability the big question slaps us – WHY???? Why us? To which there is no real answer.

So a day a time .... step by step, thankful for the "Sharon's" in the world and the kindness we ca bestow on each other.

April 12

NANCY'S JOURNAL

The MRI shows that the tumor is shrinking, such a relief and not one I expected would be the result. But what no one else knows is that it's coupled with the life he has to lead, which is hard. His body is different, often uncooperative. His speech is slurred, he has side effects from the steroids: swollen face, neck and eyes, having to poop all day, bad breath, interrupted sleep, low frustration tolerance, no romance any more, confusion and none of this will ever get any better. That is the real part.

And the pain of our children. I watch them see their father acting strangely and I alternate between wanting to protect them and being mad at them for not being more tolerant, even though I understand.

April 14

NANCY'S JOURNAL

Still the confusion of when to be a part of the world and when not to be. People reach out to me but sometimes I just wish that I could hide and not have people invite me over. I don't feel friendly. I don't feel normal and honestly, I don't want to listen to someone else's problems. It sounds mean but I just don't have the energy.

April 15

NANCY'S JOURNAL

Greg and I met with a lovely woman whose husband died of a

brain tumor a year ago. I felt better after talking to her. I think I need to just expect the best instead of expecting my world to crumble any minute. We many have a long time and I need to remember that and in fact, assume it! I am just recovering from the initial stages of grieving and loss. It is possible that this relatively easy phase we are in can last a long time.

April 18

NANCY'S JOURNAL

I have succeeded in my attitude that this will last a while and be ok. I am letting go of the gloom expectation a little bit. It takes conscious effort not to expect the next boom to fall any time. I am feeling more like my old self. But this afternoon when I came home Greg was crying. It is harder on him than he lets on. He says he is just tired of it all and after a vacation with other normal families the loss of what we had is accentuated.

April 28

NANCY'S CARINGBRIDGE LETTER

Yesterday we went to the monthly brain tumor support group. This time we separated into "patients and caregivers." It was wonderful for me! Oh, how I wish I could have this opportunity more often. I can only liken it to having been in some obscure foreign country for seven months, doing a home stay, and suddenly talking and interacting with someone from my own country.

The path of the caregiver is a unique experience. I am grateful that Greg and I can share so much together so far on this wild ride, but two side roads branch off of our one road and only I can navigate mine and he his. It is hard work to learn how to walk down my own side road and it is lonely. I can have companions on it for a while, but I must learn the intricate, complicated answers on my own. I am sometimes confident on my road and also sad and terrified. I can be graceful as I walk but more often I feel awkward and tentative.

I look different on the outside compared to how I feel on the inside. I wonder sometimes if I am such a good actress that I fool even myself. I know this skill is what enables me to function. As I spoke and listened yesterday, I also heard how normal this is and that is a comfort.

I am more aware of the layers of learning that this experience gives us. We have had the "shock and awe" part. Now we are in another phase of living with what we have, knowing a lot about how it will end but not knowing when. It is all about living each day to the fullest and I think we have been good students of that school. There is the challenge of always wondering when the ground will rattle again. How do we dream now? Can we plan another trip? Will we have 3 months or 10 years together?

Lilly has decided to leave school until next fall. It is too hard for her to be away from us and I am proud of her ability to articulate that decision. Emma has finished her junior year at McGill and come home. Clara is putting in 12-hour days: in school full time, running track and now taking driver's ed class every evening. All three girls have employment for the summer so that seems good.

CHAPTER 10

MAY 2011

No, I'd never been to this country
before. No, I didn't know where the roads
would lead me. No, I didn't intend to
turn back.

—Mary Oliver, "No, I'd Never Been to This
Country"

May 6

NANCY'S JOURNAL

I don't think I will ever figure out how to do this. When I worry, Greg will suddenly have a day where he seems fine, like his old self, and I think maybe I am just making this whole thing up. It is not that I want him to be sick, I *do not*, but I can't figure out what I need to manage and track and what I don't.

True, he can do most things – but then he is so tired. I feel I can only expect of him what he is willing to do and that is inconsistent – a word I do not like. The question becomes, "Where do I fit? Where do my needs get met now?"

Sometimes I feel like he is almost gone from me. He is trying hard to be all things to all people and all things to himself but I get left out of that picture.

May 8

NANCY'S JOURNAL

Mother's Day… Oh why can't I enjoy my life more? I am irritable and don't deal with people well and then I feel terrible. Greg is friendly and makes everyone feel good. I have more trouble with people and don't feel like I am any good to be around.

May 11

GREG'S CARINGBRIDGE LETTER

It has been a while since I have written which is probably a good thing …. I have been pretty much functioning at the same level for the last few months for which Ii am very grateful. In June we will do another MRI to check the any development and to know what happens without using steroids – slowly still weaning off them – a huge relief!

Also, in June, after our oncologist said, "Why wait?" when we mentioned we wanted to see our friends in England in September – "you are doing great now." We were able to finally have our British Airways miles work for us. So are going the first week of June and our three girls, now older and more mature will take care of themselves! A new era!

Speaking of our girls it is wonderful having them home – they are cooking excellent meals in the evenings, helping out around the house, relieving Nancy of extra work … at 16, 19, and 22 they are becoming young adults! For Mother's Day they treated her like a queen. We had family circle at the Land Bank Park and talked about needs for summer, how we are all handling this fucking tumor that sits like a quiet beast in my head and how we can support each other ... tears and sweetness – I feel SO supported by my immediate family and my extended family!

My days are varied, rich with people and I am working on projects that I enjoy including finishing up the old VW.

Some days are tough – yesterday morning where everything I touched, I dropped, could not button my shirt, and my tolerance for my "sickness" was gone – finally I just took a two hour nap after a good scream and throwing a few things around!

It is amazing all the things that are difficult – especially with your strength robbed by the steroids. With chemo and 4 or 5 other drugs I have to just deal with whatever chemical soup is in my body!

End of this week our family is off to see Desmond Tutu – one of my heroes and then back to our island which is threatening to really open up and become spring between lots of rain. The boating season is just beginning which now with more time I am hoping to get out to our beautiful camping islands – my spiritual home!

So still on the roller coaster – determined to be the outlier of brain tumor patients – I am now 9 months out from prognosis of a year to live, I am feeling good, strong, for the most part able to deal with the changes in my body- and feeling like i have lots of time left, however, I still am filling my days and trying to squeeze what I can out the hours and minutes of a day – that includes my cat naps to keep my energy up.

Life is SO precious .... this is my first spring without a million things to do for school – May is always busy ...truly I have time to smell the flowers, see the brilliant reds of the tulips, watch the birds come to our feeder and maybe when I have time – do nothing!

May 16

NANCY'S JOURNAL

Greg has limited energy these days and I think we all need and want what he has, for our family. He has such a desire to be the pleaser and focus all of his attention on each visitor but then there is not much left for us...how to do this?

May 24

NANCY'S JOURNAL

He is trying to wean from the steroids, but it has such an effect on his functioning. I really hope he can get off of them but it is very hard to watch. He is so discouraged and frustrated in our daily life. Everything he tries to do is hard and he ends up feeling badly. His hand doesn't work and he has no energy. He is trying to push through it. We have this trip planned and I don't see how he can do it at this rate.

Chapter 11

June 2011

. . . Build,
use everything, build, so terror
may be turned to bigness and even beauty.

—Rilke, from "Mein Leben hat das gleiche
Kleid und Haar"

June 1

Greg's CaringBridge Letter

Tattoos — I never thought about getting one until we were in Hawaii and saw that everyone had one there... Even the small town on Molokai had a tattoo parlor! It is amazing what you think of doing when you have a brain tumor! So I went in to check out the tattoo artist there but he was off to the big island for a couple of days. Probably a good thing because I wanted to get a Northwest Indian design of a grizzly on my left shoulder, close to my heart. As life has it's twists and turns, at about the same time Lilly, Clara and Emma were scheming on Facebook to get tattoos to honor me with a remembrance of their Dad permanently on their bodies. The idea they were throwing back and forth was a grizzly bear on their shoulder! On a trip to Corvallis two weeks ago (just Lilly and Emma), they visited a tattoo parlor that

Emma had recommended by a friend ("He gets all of his tattoos there"). Both Lilly and Emma returned home with a small grizzly bear tattooed on their shoulders – the design Emma made from a pin I wear and the addition of her artistic skills. I was deeply moved! As they said now they will carry me throughout their life! Clara, who is only sixteen, has to go with a parent so she and I are going to get one as well... Nancy will get a henna version and has told me she has a grizzly permanently tattooed on her heart.

I seem to be maintaining my same level of functioning with brief period of trying get off steroids – I have gone back to a small dose of steroids after being totally exhausted when I went from the 6 mg to 0. So until my next MRI on June 10th I am guessing that the tumor has not decided to grow yet and I have a good summer ahead!

We are now on the plane headed for New York and then England. I am looking forward to seeing old haunts, friends, and visiting the school I taught at in 2002 -2003! Meanwhile our girls will hold down the fort – working and going to school.

Now June is officially here I am looking forward to summer, time with family and friends, trips to islands and mountains. Summer is a very sweet time in the Pacific Northwest!

June 1

NANCY'S CARINGBRIDGE LETTER

Sometimes it seems we are in a bubble and "the big reality" swirls around us but we are protected from it. We received the monthly chemo pills in the mail as we pack for our trip. When I saw the package in the mailbox, my mind wondered, "What would Group Health be sending us in a padded envelope?"

I am fascinated by the disconnections our minds make to save us from the constant reality of what is.

Yesterday, before we left, we went to school to hear some of the senior project presentations. In one presentation, a courageous young woman spoke about her eating disorder that was exacerbated by the sudden death of her father. Another presentation was a strong young man who set out to learn about Northwest Indian carving as a tribute to his father, also a carver, who died of a glioblastoma when he was five. The last was one of Greg's former students for whom he has been a strong mentor in photography. She conceived of the idea, "Grieving and Loss of a Loved One," shortly after Greg was diagnosed. It has helped her to come to terms with his illness and I think it was helpful to the room full of students and staff who were listening. She interviewed him and others for the project and was sensitive and articulate in her presentation. Emma sat with her head resting on Greg's shoulder. Clara was stoic. Greg and I listened appreciatively as we worked to hold the deep emotions at bay.

It is all so crazy and wild. In some ways our realities are stark and almost pre-determined and yet here we are on a plane on our way back to the England that we love. Sometimes I wonder how a human psyche can hold these paradoxes and if mine will really hold up? Do I have several fully formed identities inside me that I can access at different times or just such strong multiple emotions?

Our girls did not want to be left alone while we came on this trip and yet they are happy for us. They really "get" what this trip means to us: to re-visit, together, a world that was home to one of the best years we have spent together. It is time to board the plane.

June 3

NANCY'S JOURNAL

I can't believe we are here! What a sweet reunion with Jenny and Malcolm and Gaye and Dave on the way from London to Exeter. It is hard to be away from the girls and I worry about them all the time, but at the same time, I am just so happy to be away with Greg and be able to share this deep feeling we have for our year in England and all it gave our family. It was an adventure in which we all were on equal, insecure footing: making new friends, learning a new way of life and having unique experiences. It changed each of us and brought our family close together in a lasting way. It was also a time that Greg loved as a teacher. He was so unique in the British system and was a genuine breath of fresh air which was so good for him.

June 5

NANCY'S CARING BRIDGE LETTER

Today, the principal of Greg's school hosted a big potluck for us and all of the teachers we knew came to see us. It was just amazing to feel all of the love and care they hold for us, even at this great distance. I know it was great for Greg to be honored again for the impact he made at that little village school eight years ago.

June 6

NANCY'S CARING BRIDGE LETTER

This morning, we hopped on a train to Penzance to meet a woman we'd learned about who does healing work. We were a world away from our difficult world of home as we sat on the train and watched the lush, picturesque scenery. I thought of all of the train travel we did in the year we lived here. It is a time that seems so innocent now. Our children were young, we were younger and the word brain tumor was as remote as any.

We got to our hotel, which looks like it is from a picture book. Greg took a nap and I drank my cup of English tea while gazing out the window at the coastline and the water framed by lace curtains. Now, it is sunny and warm and the sky over the water is brilliant blue. I feel so grateful to have this luxury of time with no one to take care of.

June 7

NANCY'S CARING BRIDGE LETTER

We met Heather Bray today, the healer we had learned about. Greg lay on a table while she floated a pendulum over his body. I observed the process and was amazed at how intuitive the pendulum was as it passed over him. It found many "working patterns" as it went over the left side of his body, most affected by the tumor. We chose healing stones for Greg and placed them on his body. While I doubt that this process can eradicate the tumor, it led me to think about what "healing" really means. We felt so loved and safe there. Perhaps the healing was on a spirit level rather than the physical plane. It was an honor to be with Heather as she shared her gift of healing. I wished so much that I could be on that table – much in my heart and soul needs strong medicine.

June 8

NANCY'S JOURNAL

What a full week it has been. Has it only been a week? It feels like much more than a week. I know the girls being alone is stressful for them and I feel a strong need to get back to them but I do so hate to leave this world of deep friendships and memories. Sad goodbyes. I know we are all wondering if this will be the last time? I know that it will be for Greg, and it rips my heart out.

June 9

GREG'S CARINGBRIDGE LETTER

Back in America.... jFK airport for the night ... home tomorrow after an MRI ... I think I am lost in transition ... feeling frustrated with this tumor I am carrying around ... every action I take with my left hand is compromised – from picking something off the floor on the airplane to trying to dress myself. I make a fist and my fingers are numb! I don't like it but cannot get away from it!

In good Jewish tradition – on one hand the whole situation is enough to drive one crazy yet on the other hand I just had a wonderful time in England with lots of energy (I went back on a small amount of steroids which made all the difference, i think) visited old friends- laughing, barbecues, visited my old school (where I taught), got trounced in ping – pong by my buddy Cipri, and even had time to go to Cornwall by train to visit a lovely English woman, Heather Bray, who has long followed a strong calling as a healer. She uses crystal, pendulum, and Bach flower remedies in her practice.

And she is also a Quaker and member of a meeting that is housed in the oldest Quaker meeting house in England.

As we gazed out the windows for the 3 hour train journey, we delighted in seeing the English countryside dressed in it's finest many shades of green.

June 9

NANCY'S CARINGBRIDGE LETTER

We loved our time in England, reuniting with old friends and catching up on the joys and struggles of life over the intervening years. We literally and figuratively walked in the footsteps of our unique and special year and savored each moment.

Thanks to the efficiency of modern technology, we were often in touch with the girls. Along with a bit of support from our friends, they coped well on their own and gave us a gift for which we are deeply grateful. It was a big job for them and they took it on willingly. We are quite sure that we will be appreciated when we return!

June 13

NANCY'S CARINGBRIDGE LETTER

We finally heard from the oncologist today who tells us that the results of the MRI are that everything looks pretty much the same. He recommends that Greg stay with the same chemo regimen and have another MRI in two months. It is good news, but still kind of a discouraging week for Greg. No matter how "good" the news is, he is still forced to live with a brain tumor and there are many ways that it is difficult. He puts a lot of energy into maintaining his spirits and does that incredibly well but there are periods where it all takes its toll. We are in one of these periods.

June 26

NANCY'S JOURNAL

We had so much fun together in England, walking through our old life with all of the memories. It was perfect and beautiful. It was good to get home to the girls as well, but then chemo and a B-A-D week, really bad and *sad*. How wrong it all feels now. It is just not supposed to be this way.

We went to the school staff retirement party but Greg is not retiring as he had planned. He had to leave. No one really knew how to handle it so no one did handle it well.

Greg is changing, or maybe his changes just seem more cemented. He is different and sometimes I am used to it and other times I look at him and it is *so* hard. I love him more than ever but it is hard to feel attraction at this stage and that makes me feel terrible.

June 29

NANCY'S JOURNAL

Hard days -- then realistic view from neuro-oncologist: he shouldn't be driving and the tumor will not be going away. Good news is that it is stable.

So much to integrate. Greg is sad and frustrated with all he can't do. Not sure he will give up driving, but he may drive less. It is another level of recognizing the loss and maybe coming to terms with it?

He will take it as well as he can but I am not confident that he will be able to integrate it all. My process is so different than his. There are huge losses for me but I have people to talk to who have been through this and he does not. All of those who have had the same tumor have died.

I don't know sometimes what is the right thing to say to him and I often feel like I say the wrong thing, which makes him sadder somehow. The aspects of life that make him feel most valuable are exactly the things he can't do.

At least he can and does have relationships and he can still maintain those well.

CHAPTER 12

JULY 2011

Hold fast to dreams
For if dreams die
Life is a broken-winged bird
That cannot fly.

—Langston Hughes, "Dreams"

July 5

NANCY'S CARINGBRIDGE LETTER

I am reflecting today on these ten and one-half months since we started this journey and I continue to wonder about so much of it. Where have we come from? What have we learned? Where are we going? How does anyone live with this much uncertainty? Do I have what it takes to face the future?

I have recently realized that we are living in the "middle phase" now.

The crisis is over and the shock has worn off. Our mailbox is not filled with cards daily, our phone does not ring more than our normal, we aren't the center of attention everywhere we go, we cook our own meals, do most of our own work, and Greg doesn't really need much medical attention at this time. There are times where I don't constantly think about the fact that Greg has a brain tumor.

Never did we allow ourselves to dream that we would have summer days, camping trips, that Greg would be chain sawing and that we would have what often feels like a normal routine: girls here, working, arguing, laughing with us, me working in my garden, cooking, cleaning, sewing, taking my walks, Greg working on the myriad of projects necessitated by our rural lifestyle in a self-built home. *Yet* while we are living this normal life, we are changed, oh, so, changed.

A year ago, Greg and I talked of our dreams for retirement and the girls looked optimistically to their futures. We now must question every thought of the future. Every step forward we take, we wonder, "what if?"

We live with constant questions. We live with a huge loss. Everything is more difficult for Greg, who, a year ago was the captain of a very competent ship. He has always been able to accomplish anything he set his mind to and now the simplest tasks are a struggle. There are days of deep sadness and confusion. And we know that any day we could turn the corner and here will be a loss we still can't imagine.

Yet we have so many blessings and advantages. Greg also feels good a lot of the time and he can do much of what he enjoys. Our life continues to embody paradox. The task of learning to live in paradox *is* daunting, but it is our life. We all put one foot in front of the other and carry on. The sun rises every morning and sets every night and here we are.

We are tentatively learning to look ahead a bit. We think about another trip in the fall, Thanksgiving, maybe even a family trip in February. I am find that the real learning for me is how to really live with all of the uncertainty and by that I mean, really live, rather than always waiting for the next MRI to plan something fun. I am taking baby steps in this learning, never sure of myself.

We had a family visit to the neuro-oncologist last week. She could answer a lot of questions the girls had and a few more of ours. The tumor is stable and we had confirmation that it will not go away. Stable is the best we can expect. It is always a bit sobering to look at that MRI and see that tumor there.

Greg and the girls joined in on the 4th of July parade yesterday in the finished VW and Clara got her driver's license on Friday.

Greg takes off next week with a bunch of 8th and 9th graders on a sailing trip! There are four adults and ten kids. It is, perhaps, a wee bit ambitious but that never has stopped Greg. The kids can't wait to spend time with him again.

It is one of life's deep mysteries how we can truly hold each other up by bearing witness to each other's pain and joy.

July 7

NANCY'S JOURNAL

Greg and I met on this day in 1987. I am in Seattle for a one-night retreat. No one to take care of or worry about. I got to sleep as long as I wanted to. We had a rough weekend with all three girls flipping out and screaming and yelling. It was awful. Greg has angry outbursts at least once a day. This is the part no one else really knows or sees. I absorb it all and it breaks my heart somewhere. I can totally understand Greg's frustration and anger but I hate it. He does not take it out on anyone else but I hear him throwing things outside, yelling and cussing. I feel totally helpless. A voice in me says, "He has to go through this and you can't help him." Maybe I can't – but I should be able to help my children.

July 9

NANCY'S CARINGBRIDGE LETTER

Here is what Lilly said about the Grizzly claw tattoo that she and Emma now share.

"The Grizzly Bear is a symbol of strength and good health. This is my dad's Greg Ewert spirit animal. I got this tattoo in honor of him. My dad is a fighter and I wanted to get something to have forever as a symbol of his strength and courage. Even when he is no longer with me physically, he will always be with me in spirit. My dad has given so much to this world; he is a teacher, a friend, a role model and, most importantly, a dad to many people other than me. I love and respect him more than words will ever allow me to say."

July 19

NANCY'S JOURNAL

I went away to Quaker yearly meeting with Clara and Emma and had a good time. Saw lots of old friends and appreciated everyone asking about Greg. Then home – sad – I almost forgot what it is really like. It is easy to be away and tell everyone who asks that Greg is stable, doing ok, camping, boating but we come home and re-learn what "stable" means.

It means he is tired, sad and angry that he has a brain tumor that rules his life. It rules all of our lives and isolates us into another world. Greg never feels good. He is not joyous very often. He says to others that he is fine but he does not feel fine. There is always diarrhea. He struggles to do the simplest of tasks and just to maintain. There is always the fear. It never leaves us.

But there are moments of joy – the moment of his telling a story, the moment of driving the newly refurbished VW in the parade. My life is one huge balance scale of joy with deep sorrow all at once. Never a moment of happiness without a concurrent moment of sadness.

Are there other people in my situation who are joyful? Do I look at the dark side too much? Maybe these moments of joy are all we ever had? Maybe we just had the illusion of having a joyful life when all we ever had was moments of joy.

July 25

NANCY'S JOURNAL

I dreamed that I was in an airplane and it suddenly crashed with no warning. I was thrust forward and I slid hard and want head first into something, then stopped. My head crashed really hard...so hard that my teeth fell out. I had all sorts of instant thoughts – oh, I will have a head injury if I live through this? And where is Greg? I knew he was behind me somewhere and I wanted to tell him I loved him.

CHAPTER 13

AUGUST 2011

. . . What you fear
will not go away: it will take you into
yourself and bless you and keep you.
That's the world, and we all live there.

—William Stafford, "For My Young Friends
Who Are Afraid"

August 4

GREG'S CARINGBRIDGE LETTER

Wow! I have three beautiful, insightful daughters.... Last week the
four of us spent a couple of nights out together for some Dad and daugh-
ter time. Over an excellent stirfry in the galley of a 30' sailing boat, we
talked about some of the harder questions....

what do you want to do with me while we still can? what do you want
to accomplish in your life? In caring for Marm (term of endearment
invented by the girls for Nancy...also known as Marmscicle or
Marmble), I want them to work together as a team unlike my own
family....and to truly look after her. We all vowed to take advantage of
each day never knowing when things are going to change. A sweet,

necessary evening....and we need more. It is so easy for time to get swallowed up by the demands of daily life.

August....a year ago I started feeling something was wrong but like a good representative of the male species, I ignored it until it was SO obvious. And then the diagnosis on August 20th...."average, one year" with my condition. Well I am coming on a year now and I am still fully alive though not 100% close enough to do most of what I want to do. What a year, the pulling together of my immediate family and extended family, the death of my father and being totally blessed living in and being supported by the our island community, receiving letters and gratitudes for my work....I feel very blessed.

The first night in the hospital, I made a list of what I wanted to do for my family before the tumor incapacitates me....I have completed that list so now I just want more time to spend with family and friends. In the past year I have let go of all of the things (almost) that are not important to me and am trying to find peace and resolve with what I feel needs my attention. Even though my disability is small, (loss of balance, some speech difficulties, loss of strength on my left side) there are days that are SO frustrating. I am not ready to accept and acquiesce to this tumor yet. I still have to believe that I might be the clinical study for having such a stubborn brain that even cancer cannot grow there.

So for the most part I am doing well. I am grateful to be alive and have another MRI on Thursday to hopefully confirm that. As always, I feel so blessed to be in this supportive loving community both near and far.

August 5

NANCY'S CARINGBRIDGE LETTER

Yesterday was the "longest day." We drove to Seattle and back, fighting too much traffic, for Greg's MRI. We got the results today and it was not the news we hoped for. How we wished to hear our favorite word of 2011: "stable!" Instead, we heard that the tumors are growing enough to warrant a change in treatment.

The new drug is a bi-monthly infusion. It is our last resort of treatment. This is news we knew we would one day hear but it is devastating nonetheless. We are all together today and that is good. We need each other more than ever.

August 9

NANCY'S CARINGBRIDGE LETTER

Often there is a wild storm raging inside my head and heart. It feels like my psyche is a giant box of jigsaw puzzle pieces that are from a bunch of different puzzles so they can't fit.

Greg has a growing brain tumor of the "most aggressive" kind that will surely take his life away. This is a staggering truth, and yet he is away on the annual "Dads and Kids Boat Trip" with beloved friends and his girls. This yearly tradition has gone on for *seventeen* years. Last year's trip was just prior to his diagnosis, and *we* all thought that would be his last.

Now it has been a year: a year so full that it is defies imagination.

Oddly, after the first 6 weeks of radiation, a brain tumor does not require us to spend much time in the medical world. We don't have to go into the hospital often, Greg is not exceedingly "sick" and we have had the privilege of spending our time here in our wonderful home and community or on some pretty darn good travel adventures.

I shudder to sense the change that is coming.

We will go into the oncology center every two weeks now for an infusion. Going into the hospital fills me with trepidation. I hate it. *It* blasts the comforting illusion of normalcy into pieces. There is only one reason we are there and that reason is that Greg has a fatal disease.

Here I sit in my kitchen during this heavenly quiet week, gathering my strength. I am trying to focus on gratitude and moments of joy. It is almost trite to try to put into words, but surprising to me how many small moments of beauty I notice now.

Seeing Greg's shining face as the boat full pulled out into the water yesterday morning, the orange nasturtiums on my deck, the smiling face of my dear yellow lab, the sunsets and the moon, poetry and music, the way the sun glints through the forest: these are all moments of profound beauty and joy for me and I am working hard on cementing these moments into my psyche.

Emma's flight back to Montreal is on August 21st. She has one more semester. She is agonizing about what to do: should she continue or stay home? Clara made a recent decision that she would try for a semester abroad this January. She knows now that she might not be able to go. Lilly dropped out the last quarter of her first year of college and now needs to go back in September. Will she make it through this time?

These questions are so big for these young women taking flight. We have been given the gift of more time than we imagined, and now we are so greedy for more.

August 29

NANCY'S CARINGBRIDGE LETTER

It has been a year. A year since I innocently had a crazy 60th birthday party, not knowing that a day later, our lives would change forever.

Some days, Greg feels fragile and teary. On those days I feel distanced and experience a more business-like approach as the caretaker, the one who can make everything work.

Then a day will come when I fight the tears all day. I still wake up some mornings and forget reality for a few minutes until that sinking feeling hits me. It is as though in my dream life, I have been given respite – that is a gift.

We weathered the "year anniversary" and my birthday with a lovely gathering around a fire ring with a circle of friends of all ages where we shared gratitude for the gifts we have all received in this complicated and poignant year. Many of the gratitudes were to Greg for all he means to the people who love him. All three girls were there. It was a magical evening with food, margaritas and music to celebrate. It was all so fitting and so our island. A night to be deeply grateful to live in this community.

A few days later we got Emma off to Montreal where she found an apartment and moved in. Settling into a temporary home is a relief to her, and of course, to us. It was a sad departure, but she will be home for a long weekend in October and that is not so far away.

Greg had his first Avastin infusion, it went well and was uneventful. It is not expected that he will feel any different right away.

We made a fun evening of it by going to a cabaret circus dinner theater called Teatro Zinzanni to celebrate our twenty-third wedding anniversary. We are doing our best to have fun.

Fall is fast approaching. There seems to be no reason not to just try to live as normally as possible. With all of this in mind every day, Lilly and Clara continue with their plans for school and study abroad.

We committed to a trip on October and I signed on to be in a play in November. My logical mind tells me we might be pushing our luck a bit but, honestly, there is no other way. Logic does not mean much anymore.

We hope and pray that Greg will be in the 40 percent of people who respond well to Avastin. Compared to most folks in his situation, the guy is truly remarkable. He just keeps going and going.

The summer with the girls is already full of many rich memories. A year ago we did not think we would have that. We live in full awareness of the unexpected gift of more time than we imagined and it only seems right to make the most of it. Gifts abound and continue to surprise us as we walk this road.

CHAPTER 14

SEPTEMBER 2011

. . . The gods
allow us only a moment of indulgence,
a little taste, right before, in their infinite
and merciless wisdom, they take it back.

—Danusha Laméris, "Chance"

September 3

NANCY'S CARINGBRIDGE LETTER

Greg celebrated the one-year anniversary of his craniotomy by going to an "Air Show" with two of his pilot buddies in Johnson City, Idaho. They left with food, tents, sleeping bags and wine. I am sure he got to pilot the plane a bit (not with the blessing of any of his doctors, I might add) which added a lot to that happiness meter.

The new oncologist we met told us that although the average amount of time that Avastin works for glioblastoma patients is six months, he has one patient who is doing well after a year of treatment. If there is one, there can be two, and we all know who #2 is!

Today I was walking and remembering a walk on that same beach this time last year. I was so raw and felt like my whole world was crumbling. It is amazing to me to walk on that beach today and feel resilience. I am in awe of the unexpected blessings amidst the anguish.

Our lives are ever changing, but I wonder if we have all reached a level of acceptance? It is scary to proclaim anything so lofty but it is what I have felt in the last few days. I am eager to hear how the old pilot is feeling after his big adventure.

September 7

GREG'S CARINGBRIDGE LETTER

Indeed it has been a year! School Istarted today and for the second time in 34 years I did not have group of students wondering who this teacher is and what is he going to do to me! I do miss the kids – I don't miss the work one has to put into teaching.

My trip to Idaho was much more than an air show – it was bunch of renegades flying their small planes from all over the West into the base camp at Johnson Creek, a 5,000 foot elevation airstrip in Idaho. From there we would fly into small dirt strips – mostly mining access strips dotted with the remains of old buildings, machinery ,and rusted mechanical parts l. I rate that morning of dirt strip hopping as one of the best in my life! It had all the elements of things I love. I was of course the happy passenger, not the pilot but this is what I dreamed of doing with my pilots license. Thanks Steve, Ron and Dave!

So dreams – I have been called a dreamer – the person with ideas who makes things happen ...which is how I see myself as well. Many years ago I realized I don't have time for all I wanted to do so I shortened my list and dropped what was unrealistic. The cruel reality of a brain tumor is that it takes away your" future" – my dreams. I have to scale way back because of my physical realities. Even though it may seem like I am doing a lot that is a lot for someone with a brain tumor – not for a normal active person. When I lose my balance getting out of my tent, fall and break my tent pole and then spend an hour trying fix it with a hand that does work right I just want to scream! Then reality hits me in the face!

Dreams . There are many challenging pieces in this brain tumor puzzle. I have my shortened list that with the latest shift of a growing tumor, the new drug that will help but according to all the trials not for that long – don't get me wrong I am not giving up hope or the fight – but I am trying to face reality. So I am looking at what I can do...

I am going to throw myself into writing my story for my grandkids(or have Nancy type while I talk!). Thinking about the best days of my life has set off a flood of fine memories – I want to record those. (I am staying away for now the worst days of my life)!

I will spend time with close friends and family – I will do goofy projects that I enjoy – using my hands has always been therapeutic – I will teach a small math group at school and perhaps help some kids in the darkroom at school. Also, I have recently learned how to make platinum prints and want to explore that more. That may sound ambitious but when you are "retired" there is a lot of time.

I have been struggling with the thought of my body leaving this earth – I am SO not ready. It feels SO unreal that something is growing on my brain that will eventually kill me ... I know I will find a way to walk down that path but I sure want to put it off as long as I can. It reminds me of eating fried liver that Mom would serve us – I know it was necessary but I sure struggled to swallow it!

Speaking of Mom – Happy birthday – you would be 91 if you were alive today!

And I am grateful to be alive for one more day !

September 10

NANCY'S JOURNAL

Terrifying day in the ER…don't know what it is…maybe a seizure? We are waiting to find out. Feels like a new game and very scary. I am so tired and can't make much sense of it all. But I know I am really scared. Scared of what this means, scared about the future, scared about not knowing and having to make decisions without knowing. Scared this will happen again. On the way home, I found a bench on the ferry away from everyone else and cried the whole 45 minute trip.

September 11

NANCY'S CARINGBRIDGE LETTER

Greg had been feeling good over the last week or so. He had his second Avastin infusion on Thursday and it seemed to go well. Then he had a long day on Friday at the Wooden Boat Festival. It was a fun but long fourteen-hour day in the hot sun.

We got up early on Saturday. Clara and I had plans to go off island together for an overnight and a bit of mom/daughter time. Greg was planning to go out later in the day for some full moon camping on a nearby island with his ever-devoted good friends. He left the house to go outside to work on a building project and felt and seemed fine.

About thirty minutes later he came stumbling into the front door with blood dripping from a small cut on his head. He was disoriented and couldn't walk very well. It was terrifying. He said he had fallen a few times outside. He did not really hurt himself except for a gnarly superficial scrape on this arm. We called our oncologist and our friend Eric came over to help. Greg was unreasonable for a few hours so it was helpful to have him here.

After several phone calls, and a plane ride from a friend to the hospital, we spent the rest of the day trying to determine what had happened. He gradually got back to normal after the steroids which seems to point to a sudden onset of brain swelling but we don't know why.

We came home in the evening and of course, no fun mom/daughter time or camping under the full moon. Greg feels fine today and, other than not driving, he is back to his normal self.

It is unnerving to wonder if it could happen again. It was upsetting for me to see him like that and just when I was breathing a sigh of relief! We are crossing our fingers now that it was just an isolated incident but we will be on pins and needles for a while.

September 12

NANCY'S CARINGBRIDGE LETTER

Our beloved neuro-oncologist has moved to Boston, but yesterday I remembered that her last words to me were: "Feel free to email me if you ever have any questions." I wrote to her describing the incident.

She got back to me right away and said she is almost certain that Greg had a seizure. This affirmed my first thought because we have been warned so often to look for that. She further explained that confusion is a common after effect so it all fits with what happened.

It is not good news and really discouraging for Greg. It means no driving and that is just indescribable in its impact. It can be a sign of tumor growth. It is controllable with medication so perhaps we do not have to go through this again. Now, we are just trying to absorb this new development and I feel scared.

September 14

NANCY'S JOURNAL

Driving last night home from Corvallis after dropping Lilly off – We took off after dinner and drove at night listening to music and podcasts. It just felt like we were in a lovely little vacuum. It was deep dark outside and I felt like we could just keep driving forever and never stop, never go home again, drive away from the feeling of doom. Home is where the bad things have happened: sickness, the seizure, and the hospital. That thought of just driving away from it all was so perfect for a few minutes.

I feel so angry lately that we can't be normal any more. Greg had felt good for a couple of weeks and then *zap!* it got taken away, just when we had a breath of relief.

September 15

GREG'S CARINGBRIDGE LETTER

Again a short entry here from me ,,, I never have had a seizure before it was one more life experience we all should know about – in my case it lasted a little over two hours and I was acting drunk, unstable and in the end had no memory of that time. Even to the point of making a phone call I do not remember. So emergency room, friend flew us over to Ana cortes and a long day we are now sorting out what happened. (I can't tell you how frustrating typing is!)

So I guess this is now a new phase – I grudgingly accept my driving , (even on our island), being taken away... hard but necessary. I will have to rely on friends coming to me and my dear wife and daughter to help haul me around. Fortunately our island is small and my errand needs are minimal.

New anti-seizure meeds are brutal – make me tired all day – in process of adjusting those. Frankly, I am tired of filling my body with chemicals – sometimes it seems it would be better just let my body deal with the tumor and fuck all the intervention!

But then my three girls and Nancy come into focus and I will stay alive as long as I can. Just dropped Lilly off at OSU for her second year and she is very happy to be back. Great scene in Kappa Kappa Gamma ... friends, healthy atmosphere, lovely living quarters! I think college freshmen shoal do there first year with virtual glasses and avoid all the shit they have to go through, and all the booze they have to drink! Can a virtual beer make you drunk?

So settling into fall with unknowns and potential pitfalls is not easy but the reality – which is in essence the problem – (in spite at times ignoring the tumor) it does raise its ugly head all the time. So I am hoping for a seizure free fall , am excited about friends and family visiting and will continue to work on a building project and writing project.

I am loathe to let summer go! It has been good to start fall without the pressure of reaching classes!

Good morning! Remember September is the best month of the year the world over – enjoy it!

September 19

GREG'S CARINGBRIDGE LETTER

I woke up thinking about heroes – large ones and quiet local heroes. I want to honor my heroes. Years ago I heard a storyteller who did an evening on a town's local heroes – the drugstore owner who gave the kids that could not afford it pencils, the vegetable farmer who took care of the drunks in the morning and so on. Each community has their quiet heroes who do not want recognition, they are only doing what they know is the right thing to do.

My big heroes are MLK, Mother Teresa. Robert Kennedy (he would have changed the world I think!),JImmy Carter (preserved chunks of Alaska in his waning moments), and Teddy Roosevelt.

Some of my local heroes are Bree Swanson (a 9th grader with an infectious spirit of joy and fortitude), Steve Adams (a teaching colleague who taught me how to listen and is willing to jump in and help anybody at any time), Debbie Tetu and Kim Foley (they work behind the scenes at school with kids that struggle with learning and the institution), Aaron Dye (owns the local store and always has a positive attitude and will bend over backwards t help people), Holly B (she has started so many young people with their first job), White Bear (now cooking incredible food but really she is magic with words and creating drama with kids), all the people at CDCA in NIcaragua who have given their life to serve a struggling population outside of Managua and educated many young people about the world outside of USA, Anah Kate (if you do not know her get to know her!), Jamie Stephens (who has thrown heart and soul into being our commissioner), and Carol Steckler, Hugh Lawrence, Lisa Geddis, Tiffany Ferrians, and Elton Sorensen, (who all went out on a limb to begin an alternative program at our island School that changed kids and adults lives....

Those are some my local, quiet heroes – there are more of course! I would encourage people to let those people know who you honor and respect while they are alive – life is fleeting at best!

Sad this morning – don't know why ... life is precious.

September 26

NANCY'S CARINGBRIDGE LETTER

I discovered on the Internet that there is a name for how I have been feeling, which feels reassuring: I am experiencing "Caregiver Fatigue."

I am having trouble welcoming the new anxieties, questions and responsibilities. But as a friend whose husband also has a brain tumor says, "It is better than the alternative."

It is difficult to feel my normal level of enthusiasm for life these days and I do not like that. I often long for connection with others who are in my position but, really, I know it is my own individual journey. I walk every day with my sweet yellow lab and have loved riding my bike.

I continue to be deeply grateful for the loving and unending support that is directed to me and for all the support and love that sustains our family. It is a long hard road but there are many sparkling lights along the way to nurture and guide us.

CHAPTER 15

OCTOBER 2011

there was shadow, a darker shade
of the same spring green - a new flower
on this fall day, revealed within
the autumn of its own brief bloom

—Denise Levertov, "A New Flower"

October 5

NANCY'S CARINGBRIDGE LETTER

Greg's treatment continues and although we have had a few more bumps in the road, overall, his status is the same.

We are looking forward to a visit from Greg's brother, Dave, and Emma, here for Canadian Thanksgiving. Shortly after, we will take off for a Caribbean cruise with Greg's sister and brother-in-law.

October 15

NANCY'S JOURNAL

It is great to be away – it feels like a tumor vacation, too.

Fingers crossed.

October15

GREG'S CARINGBRIDGE LETTER

Living and dying ... the paradox of walking holding hands with both. The dichotomy creates vibrant tension .... How can I be doing both?

On a plane to New Orleans – looking at our beautiful country – wanting more time to play, travel, sleep under the stars! The seizures scared me... Is this the shifting point? Or just a wake up call to let me I really do have a tumor! I can live with my quality of life as it is now though there are many frustrating moments daily. I am seeing family and old friends (I think in the last month I have gotten together with four friends who go back at least 30 years!). And my brother and Emma! Now Nancy and I get a week which will include my sister, Mary and her husband, Tom.

I am angry at this tumor today – everything was falling into place for the next decade of travel, hiking, watching my girls grow up, spending time with Nancy (who continues to be amazing holding our lives together) and then this tumor shows up! And though I am beating the "average" lifespan of someone with a glioblastoma, I am selfish. I want a lot more time with more strength in my body and a mind clicking on all cylinders. The frustration with a brain tumor is that you only get worse, not better, so it is a fight not to lose any mobility or cognitive ability.

Again, I am thankful for the love support we receive, especially volunteer drivers as my driving is now restricted.

Future – my greatest wish would be to know how much time I really have ... A wish I am sure we all share. Would it make a difference? I don't know. For myself I think it would. Right now I am packing as much as I can into these days – perhaps too much ... But I am worried about the next steps!

My other wish would be to have one more summer on our island! Get into the mountains- do road trip to the Rockies. One more boat trip .... see the Southwest in the spring and if I am doing well, go to the Greek islands, ~ all dreams, but for the present I am trying to take e each day as it comes. I would love to see folks – please feel free to call – we can meet for coffee or a meal.

Fall, leaves, our wood is in thanks to the help of friends and my brother and we are ready for winter. I have one more trip to Alaska again to visit old friends- people I did a trip into the Brooks Range when I was 30!

May you be warm and peaceful

October 18

NANCY'S CARINGBRIDGE LETTER

We are spending the day at a simple, beautiful beach in Costa Maya, Mexico. The warm blue water awaits me. Greg made a beeline to begin lounging on the beach. He is doing really well and we are having the time of our lives, seriously. (And we thought we had that already in Hawaii!) The water calls.

October 20

NANCY'S JOURNAL

Greg is doing well overall on the cruise, in fact, much better than when we were at home and he was pushing his limits and working too hard.

Everything is easy and all of our needs are so taken care of. Greg and I have both had episodes of sadness – mine just the total sadness and unfairness of here we are, finally able to have some adventures on our own and this will all be taken from us.

I know I can have solo adventures someday and I will, but it is much more fun together. Greg pulls me to do things I would not do on my own. And I know it means we cannot waste a minute.

For me that also means that I really need to pay attention to enjoying being with Greg.

October 22

NANCY'S CARINGBRIDGE LETTER

Today is the last full day of our vacation. We are still on the ship. Tomorrow will be a day of trying to get home: day of phone calls to check in and be sure the girls are okay, waiting for planes, waiting for the early morning ferry on Monday.

It has been a week of relaxation, sun, a few beaches with warm blue water, new and interesting people and places, some unexpected "adventures" (like the ATV jungle ride. For some things, once is more than enough!) Lots of good talks and laughter with Greg's sister Mary and her husband Tom, and of course wonderful time for Greg and me. We travel so well together and travel has always been one of our dreams. How can it be that we have this luxury of time and experiences while warding off the ghost of the future?

This week I have felt light-hearted and free of the worries that seem to pervade our lives. Then when I least expect it, I am filled with such great sadness and anger. Why, oh why, when our whole married life has been spent building and working – kids, jobs, and we finally have time to travel and be together, does it have to be ripped out from under us?

Maybe we will have more time? It is hard not to feel cheated.

Coupled with these feelings is genuine gratitude for all we have gotten to do together. We are most fortunate. There are a lot of other less desirable paths on which this experience could have taken us.

Where these wonderful memories will go? I have been told they are indelible and will serve me when life is hard and painful.

I don't know. I hope so.

It feels sad and difficult to come home to treatment, doctors, and hospital time. But we miss our kids a *lot,* miss the dog, miss our wonderful friends who bless our adventures and provide the infrastructure to make it happen.

May this bright sun and dark turquoise water outside of our cabin carry us there.

Greg has found some table tennis buddies on the ship and just got called for another game! Off he went!

October 30

NANCY'S JOURNAL

Back home. I am thinking this morning about my future and what I will do and how I can possibly live here without Greg.

I need to stop worrying about it.

We have almost committed to an overseas trimester for Clara

in January. It gives me the creeps to think about it *but* she needs it and I know it will be great for her. It is really scary for me…the "what ifs" are enormous.

I fear being lulled into complacency after a good spell like this. The reminders come to haunt. It is a crazy reality – very crazy.

CHAPTER 16

NOVEMBER 2011

And sometimes you sense how faithfully your life
is delivered, even though you can't read the
address.

—Thomas R. Smith, "Trust"

November 5

GREG'S CARINGBRIDGE LETTER

Quality of life – that is I think we all strive for. I have been lucky –
now in my 15th month since my surgery and still being able to do most
of what I want to do (except type!).

On one hand you have to be thankful for what you do have; on the
other I am coming back from Alaska realizing my backpacking days, my
skiing days, my days where I need a strong body and good balance are
over. Of course I am over 60 but I was planning on hiking through into
woods well into my 80's. So accepting my "new normal" is still hard. I
am better these days – I am not throwing things around in frustration
and coming in the house and lying down when I start dropping things.
I remember when health was the main topic of my grandparents and I
thought I will never do that and yet here I am reporting on my health!

There is a time in our life when maintaining our body is a focus how-ever, as I think about two close friends just one coming out of eye surgery and another having a hip replacement ... we all are trying to have the best quality of life that we can! I wish I could have brain replacement! I've needed that before the tumor!

My heart and spirit are doing okay – I am not ready for the next in-stallment, the decline – I don't know how one gets ready for that. Everyday I assess not only my physical abilities but also my life on a spiritual plane. I thank this world for giving me one more day and the wonderful people in my life. In Alaska I visited friends I have known for 30 and 50 years. What a gift our history is – and our history is a fabric ofso many stories, joys and painful times, the classic coat of many colors – and important for me to revisit those people and memories. I feel like my life has been full but honestly I feel like I am being robbed of time because of this tumor. I am greedy , I want more! I want to see what type of road my girls head out on ... maybe they end up like myself on a dirt backroad lost in the extreme West or maybe the city streets of the Big Apple!

People have often said to me we are all on the path from living to dying but I can tell you there is a huge difference between the theoretical "if I had a year to live" and really having only a year to live! I am in a bit of a panic some days and other days it feels like the tumor is not even there! Crazymaking, really.

So for right now life is the same old ,same old which is what I want – I interface with the medical world every two weeks for an Avastin infusion which seems to be working in keeping the tumor at bay and in between I am visiting friends and doing projects around our place.

Nancy continues to be a saint in putting up with my rollercoaster ride of emotions and supporting our three beautiful daughters.

I deeply feel all the love and support that comes our way – thank you!

November 17

GREG'S CARINGBRIDGE LETTER

A short entry as wind, rain, and winter have wrapped its cold tentacles around us. Winter coats, hats , gloves are pulled out of drawers.

Brain tumor 101 – bad class to take...

Brain tumor 102 – even worse! The first class is about gathering information – this second class is the emotional, and psychological effects of dealing with a brain tumor which includes the extended family and friends. So now finals week is coming up and frankly I am not prepared – I don't even know how to prepare for this test. I have had a hard couple of weeks feeling my physical limitations with both energy and dexterity... I am tired of being "sick".

Nancy and I met with our "care" committee from our Quaker meeting, which has been formed to help us through the next phase – a deeply appreciated gift and for me to know that Nancy and the girls will be cared for even if I am not around. Also our islandian men tend to develop unique systems of heating, water systems and and other unusal "individualized" systems in our homes – (We believe in creativity!) it is not like city living! So we are putting in place people who can support Nancy and the girls as things fall apart and quit working. That feels good to me ...

The next phase could be a long way off or could start soon -.

We are going to gather our immediate family for Christmas this year – something I had only hoped could happen after last year's Thanksgiving gathering and here we get another opportunity.

So I very grateful to have had a good year with reasonably good quality of life. Being close to Thanksgiving I can say I am deeply grateful for being alive and for being surrounded by loving family and friends. Each day has it's challenges, some more than others and I still take each one as a blessing.

November 19

NANCY'S CARINGBRIDGE LETTER

Our lives are in a constant state of upheaval and disequilibrium. As soon as I say or even think one thing, it changes. One morning recently, I had this realization that there are so many parts of me and I am never sure who will emerge at any given moment. No sooner do I breathe a sigh of relief than it is taken away by some small or large moment.

Conversely, I can be feeling pretty scared or worried, and Greg will walk in feeling chipper and then the voice within me says, "What were you thinking? He's doing great."

It is exhausting to live with an experience like this. Every day is new and that has its beauty and also its confusion and worry, depending on the moment.

Greg is vulnerable and needs other people for help more these days. He hates not driving and it feels like it is too soon in some ways. And for those of us who worry about him, it is also a relief. It's winter and dark, which does not help my mood.

There are days when Mother Nature bestows incredible sights here on our island for us to drink up: the splendor of the droplets on the yellow leaves, the quiet and soft green forest floor, geese flying in formation. I just marveled at the blessing of living on our island and having this healing earth as my daily companion.

I reflect often these days on how it was to have our world

ripped out from under us on that fateful August day only fifteen months and a lifetime ago. And now, we have been rebuilding a new structure little by little. Some is solid and stronger than it was before and some threatens to crumble at any moment.

There is one voice that reminds me to be so grateful for the strong parts, reminds me of all I have, then there is another voice that is greedy and wants to hold on to every bit that we have "regained" and never let it go, and yet another voice who rages at how unfair life is. It is difficult to accept what we know is coming when we have been "given back" so much that we felt was taken away a year ago.

And now we look forward to Thanksgiving and Christmas. We will take a trip to Michigan, Emma will be home from Montreal for good, and Clara is making her plans for Spain in February.

It is a beautiful, cold November morning. I am in Seattle for a long awaited overnight with Clara. I remember last year being there with Greg's bald head and recent diagnosis. Greg is with Lilly for "Dad's Weekend." We never dreamed that he would have another.

November 25

NANCY'S JOURNAL

I am so cut off from my feelings lately. It is an easier place to be – probably not healthy. Maybe it's ok, I don't know. My reality is too sad and I don't know what to do with that, day after day after day. I can't imagine it the future or feel it. I feel numb.

I had a dream last night that I was trying to get somewhere that I was supposed to be. I had to swim over a body of water to get there but the current was so strong against me that no matter how hard I swam, I wasn't getting anywhere. I was frightened but I was so determined that I actually made it across.

Tonight, Greg and I went to the Christmas lighting and as we walked along I was hit with the thought that we would not be there in the same way next year. Maybe he will be there in a wheelchair? Or maybe not at all? Or maybe it will be just the same and I will be surprised. What do I know?

November 26

NANCY'S JOURNAL

Another dream – I was at a train station and looking up at an elevated track. A passenger train car was up above and it backed up and almost backed off the end of the track and kept backing until it fell off. I was surprised it did not burst into flames but as I watched it I was horrified that I had to be the one to witness this crash and tell everyone what happened.

CHAPTER 17

DECEMBER 2011

. . . For a moment
it seems possible that every frailty, every pain,
could be an opening, a crack that lets the
unexpected
reach us . . .

—Ellen Bass, "Cold"

December 3

NANCY'S JOURNAL

I feel like I am always complaining and cannot handle things. Greg is doing well – everyone seems to think so, he thinks so, so what is my problem? I spend the majority of my time either tracking something for him, for the girls, cleaning, cooking, making a meal or planning a meal, dealing with family and health details.

And on one level I am also worrying and waiting for the ax to fall. People are so supportive but then I feel strange being the recipient because I wonder why we need help when we are functioning fine.

I can also feel easily overwhelmed. When I am with people,

either my friends or out in public, I feel like I need to be more cheerful, more engaged. I don't know who I am anymore or what my identity is. I feel so changed and I don't know how to enter a situation and be who I have always been. I don't know what I have to offer.

December 4

NANCY'S JOURNAL

It is another day and it is good to remember that there is always another day. We went to a fundraiser in Seattle and had so much fun. We were able to be out as a couple and not have everyone we saw ask us how we are! No one knew! It was wonderful that no one knew!

I realize how I hate to be out in public now where everyone knows. There seems to be some response that is expected of me and that I don't fulfill. It is like being on stage without a script. In fact, I *am* in a drama with no script and I am one of the leading characters.

I know the ultimate outcome but not the middle part that I am in now, and I don't know the words that should be in that script.

December 10

NANCY'S CARINGBRIDGE LETTER

We began the involved process of decorating for Christmas last night. The house looks good and we are far from done. Greg and the girls have a holiday decorating tradition that is way over the top!

I am thinking a lot lately about how, a year ago, we had our wonderful "once in a lifetime" trip to St. Lucia. That memory lives on so strongly within all of us. Even though Greg had just finished his first three months of treatment, he was strong and feeling full of zest for life. It was just plain F-U-N. I know we all thought it might be our last Christmas together, and felt anxious about what was to come.

We have now lived a year of what was to come. Our lives are a mixture of deep gratitude for the health that Greg has had, the experience of having had another year together, coupled with the daily grieving of our losses and our aching hearts. It is work not to give in to that creeping shadow of the future.

I really cannot remember my life before this happened. I remember facts and events, but I can't remember how I felt. I don't know why this bothers me except that I just feel like I want a piece of that returned to me. It is a longing for "normalcy," for humdrum, maybe a longing not to feel so much?

It is hard to need so much and yet I have found myself caught in denying that need: "Oh, I can do all this myself, what is the big deal, everyone else has to cook, clean, go to the dump." When I succumb to that, I come up short when I am needed for the "bigger" things, like talking about hospice, widening doorways for mobility devices, or hearing someone answer the phone "Cancer Care Center."

These are just normal business, these are just routines. But on a deeper level those experiences take their toll. One minute I can handle it all and the next minute I am deeply sad and fall apart for a while. I often can't predict which moment I will be in.

It is a busy time of year for all of us as we manage our social times, our needs to be together as a family, and our needs to be privately introspective. For me, it all feels heightened. The present is ever more precious.

Thanks to many helping hands, the cabin project for Emma is coming along well. It is exciting and gratifying for Greg to be able to create a sweet space for her.

We leave for Michigan on Christmas day and we are happily anticipating family time. Clara leaves for her three-month study abroad in Spain the end of January.

Though I am feeling and expressing overwhelm, our care committee is loving and supporting us. We came home from Seattle last weekend to empty garbage cans and dinner in the fridge.

These deeds make our lives easier but what is most striking is the experience of love in action. Love in action is powerful: it can be as small as a knowing look or smile with no words or as large as the book-length list of all the simple, helpful, small kindnesses toward our family.

It is a journey unlike any other. Each of us in our family must make our own road map as we go along. We are excessively fortunate to have so much nourishment along our way. Thank you.

December 13

NANCY'S CARINGBRIDGE LETTER

Greg was encouraged by a friend to team up with him and do a photo show at a local artist's cooperative! This led to a couple of weeks of hard, fun work delving into his huge library of photos – printing, matting and framing. The opening was great and now his work is hanging in the gallery. He has been learning a new/old technique called Platinum printing which he is loving. He is getting himself set up to do more at home and is excited to have a new creative outlet.

We have had nights of bright moonlight and a whole day of sun yesterday. Gray and dark today.

December 14

NANCY'S JOURNAL

Early morning and everyone is still asleep. When Greg is asleep I can relax more. It is a trick of distancing myself from what is really happening. Greg is so unhappy all of the time now and who could expect anything different? But it makes me so sad to watch and know that the happy, zest- for-life Greg is gone now.

I am acutely sensitized to his every move and mood. I frequently have the feeling that I am not doing "enough," the "right thing," or that what I say is not helpful.

December 17

NANCY'S JOURNAL

Hard few days – very hard – Greg feels terrible and scared to death. He is convinced things are changing and that is terrifying for me to hear. I am constantly worried. I feel sad and scared all the time. Am I overdoing it? Is it really as bad as I am making it or is this all in my head? I try really hard to breathe, know we can handle whatever comes our way. I worry so much about Clara's plans to go to Spain. That is all I want now…no, I want much more. I am focused on her getting to have this experience because it is immediate and tangible.

A stable MRI report will help me relax and get over this phase. I am playing this game of not wanting to worry the girls by telling them how Greg feels. I don't feel completely good about that but I can be more forthcoming when we know more. It takes *everything* I have to put on a "cheerful" face.

December 21

NANCY'S CARINGBRIDGE LETTER

Hallelujah is the word of the day: Greg's MRI showed no new tumor growth! The guy is a statistical miracle and nothing could make us happier. "Mom, it's a Christmas miracle," says Clara and that says it all for us.

As happy as we are, I can't help but think of all of those who have lost loved ones to this terrible, wicked disease called glioblastoma. We have a friend who died just yesterday. There is no rhyme or reason to who is struck and when. Each tumor is as unpredictable as the next. There is no answer to "why."

While we rejoice tonight, we also hold in our hearts all of our kindred souls who have not beat the statistics or who are just now hearing this horrible diagnosis. We all hold them in light and love. We are thankful for our good fortune today.

CHAPTER 18

JANUARY 2012

I do not believe that sheer suffering teaches. . . . To suffering must be added mourning, understanding, patience, love, openness, and the willingness to remain vulnerable.

—Anne Morrow Lindberg

January 20

NANCY'S CARINGBRIDGE LETTER

We are cozied in our house on a gray morning with snow blanketing our world outside. We rang in the New Year with family in Michigan after a sweet Christmas on our island. It all seems like a distant memory of cookies, visits, phones ringing, kids here and there and everywhere, ordinary holiday chaos and the associated comings and goings.

January 20

GREG'S CARINGBRIDGE LETTER

This morning as I was catching up on correspondence, sitting on the hearth with my ritual cup of coffee, I read about Gary Carter, beloved former NY Mets baseball player who is struggling with a glioblastoma and just took a downturn. He was diagnosed less than a year ago and is failing. So much of the time, I feel that the tumor is so far away and then I am abruptly reminded that I live with a deadly form of cancer.

After the holidays, I wonder if there will be another one for me? At this time, the Avastin seems to be doing it's work. On the one hand, I am so grateful to be alive but on the other hand, every day is such hard work... for example, reading is difficult, it is hard to articulate my words, my balance is off, my left hand does not function properly....simple tasks become more frustrating than they are worth. Yesterday I had to give up on hanging a picture. I am better at asking for help and I have my "team" at the ready .... so many friends who consistently show up to help.

Every two weeks I spend a day at the hospital for my treatment. I have excellent medical care only a ferry ride away but in spite of that, it is still one whole day of my life every two weeks for a half hour infusion. That two weeks comes more quickly than I would like. My goal is to stay alive as long as I can. In March I will have been seizure free for six months which will mean I can drive again. My doctor, however, recommends a scooter so if I hurt someone it will only be me! (I always have wanted a vespa).

My personal project for the new year is to continue working on platinum printing using my library of negatives from 40+ years of photography. I have found a creative project that is within my capabilities and will cause less frustration. As I learn to accept my limitations, it is gratifying to have this new challenge.

January 20

NANCY'S CARINGBRIDGE LETTER

Good news about a stable tumor is balanced with the constant frustrations and limitations. We live in the "yes, and" world – having a life we thought we had to give up. Adjusting and shifting expectations daily…

I have lot more responsibility than I would have chosen. Last weekend, I was the sole driver for our weekend trip over the mountains. It was snowy and scary. Greg always did the driving under these conditions, but I gritted my teeth and did it!

We all must learn to take on aspects of this life that we don't choose. I hope to do it with as much grace as possible. It is constant work. Small earth tremors – the "big one" will come – but when?

Paradox is still the word that describes our lives. Greg and I have so much sweet time together and we value it far beyond how we ever did before. His not being able to read means that I get to read to him which is such pleasure. We have both been independent all our lives and to have to depend more on each other has meant a closeness we would have never found.

The love extended to us appears to have no bounds. Our care committee is actively working to support us spiritually and physically. It is humbling and I often do not feel worthy of it. I know this – feeling worthy of it – is a big part of the lesson for me.

January 23

NANCY'S JOURNAL

For some reason today, I just feel worn out. I have had enough. I wonder how long a person can live in this kind of limbo. Nothing ever gets better for long. There is a good day on occasion, but overall it is a slow decline. It is hard to know how much I should do to assist Greg and how much to let him do for himself. Some days, like today, the losses feel really big. I wish I had someone to talk to who is in my shoes. I want to go away and have some fun but that would just accentuate all that Greg can't do.

January 28

NANCY'S JOURNAL

Clara is off…she is in Barcelona now and having fun. Such a mix of strong emotions for me – sad about Greg and happy for her. Her leaving is a marking: at Lilly's departure for her semester abroad, our lives were not yet wrapped up in "terminal illness." Here was Clara in her bright green, so happy in the security line and Greg limping, his body noodle-like and the left side of his face sagging.

I wanted to be strong for her. I thought, "I have so much sadness that if I started crying, I could flood the airport," and I had an image of all of the people in the airport flowing out on my river of tears.

I need to breathe and shift perspective. I need to be stronger, have more faith, be more grateful, do fun things or make a nice dinner. God, it takes so much energy and I feel like I just succumb to that a lot these days. Does it take more energy to feel bad than to try to do things that make me feel better?

CHAPTER 19

FEBRUARY 2012

This laboring of ours with all that remains
undone,
as if still bound to it,
is like the lumbering gait of the swan.

—Rainier Maria Rilke

February 6

NANCY'S JOURNAL

I feel so crazy and all over the map. I just can't seem to hang on to one feeling or another for more than one minute. I worry all the time now. Greg wants to go to Spain and I think it is totally unrealistic but am I sealing his fate by making this decision? It is hard to trust his ability to make good decisions. I worry, worry, worry about everything.

February 9

NANCY'S JOURNAL

Yesterday we got the news from the neuro-oncologist that

indeed Greg's tumor is growing and that she thinks four to six months of life is optimistic. Given that she is the most optimistic of all of the doctors we have seen, this is a real blow.

And yet, almost a relief to have some solid information to make decisions with. Greg still seems so much *himself* that it is impossible for me to imagine his failing that fast. But then, less than a week ago I would have said something totally different; it seemed like he was losing ground fast.

How do we balance our lives now? How do we spend our time? How do we balance seeing family and friends with the time we need as a family? There will never be enough time and I want to have as few regrets as possible. It still feels unreal. There are many parts of me that don't believe this can really happen. I can't project what it will be like. It is terrifying. I am calling Hospice today.

February 15

NANCY'S JOURNAL

I had a dream last night that I was with a large group of people going somewhere. Greg was part of the group but somehow we split into two groups. My group was going on an airplane and Greg's group was on a street corner waiting for a bus. I was in the airport at the gate and realized there was still time for him to go with me so I ran out and was trying to find him to yell to him to come. Then a security guard came and told me I was out of the security area and I had to come back in. I could see him across all of these walls and wanted to tell him. Then I had to follow her and I got really lost.

The rest of the dream was spent trying to find the airport before my flight left and there were dozens of streets and alleys and I had no idea where I was. I was frantic. I kept asking people the way. I finally ended up in a mall café. I gave up on my flight and met a nice young woman who owned the café and talked to me all about how she started it. Then I went out with her and met some of her friends and was enjoying myself.

February 18

GREG'S CARINGBRIDGE LETTER

Recently we found out through an MRI the avastin is becoming less effective ... We are increasing my steroid dose to help counter a slight tumor growth and continuing the avastin for whatever it can still do. The paradox is the last week was my best in a month – energy back, finished Emma's kitchen, working on stories and photos!

Tumor growth is of course relative, individualistic, and unpredictable. Given that the Ewert men for generations are nearly impossible to get off this earth I figure if any one can beat the odds, I can, and I have some wonderful plans ahead of me – S.F. this weekend, some warm water/beach the end of march, picking Clara up in Spain the end of April, my niece's wedding July 7 and our17th annual boat trip in the summer! So I have plenty to reach for.

Each day I treasure and will work on filling my days with life. On our little island in the middle of a large world with billions of people struggling everyday, our little battle for life is small and insignificant. Though I was struck by a wonderful passage in the book Wind, Sand, and Stars about the importance of each human being on this planet: to honor and love those around you and those not around you. During my last Reiki session, we spoke of how I can hold dear my friends and family from far away in bubbles in space. Kind of like those eye exams when you click the button when you see the light ....I know you are all little lights out there....stars in the night sky. I like to think of people I hold dear – I don' t need to see you, just to know you are there is enough – to know that we feel our connection and love. I treasure all of the visits I have had with old friends during the last year. Email or Caring Bridge guest book is the best way to get in touch with me. My responses may be short due to one finger typing if I do not respond it would not be a personal state-ment just that time is limited but know everything sent our way is read and appreciated.

In Quaker tradition I hold my loved ones in the. Light and ask you to do the same in whatever tradition you have.

February 18

NANCY'S CARINGBRIDGE LETTER

Greg had some troubling symptoms over the last several months which led us to an appointment with a neuro-oncologist. His read of the MRI together with observation of Greg's symp-toms indicate that the tumor is progressing. Continuing on the Avastin every two weeks will help slow the process but can only slow it by so much. We know this is not a good prognosis: the other shoe has dropped.

We grapple with how to take in this new information, discern what our priorities are and how to focus on them. Sad as it is, it is a good process and we are fortunate to have this opportunity.

Emma is here and Lilly came home for a weekend. The four of us have been able to process this news together. With Clara in

Spain, it is difficult to figure out how to communicate this new development to her. It is important to all of us that she sees the program through till the end of April.

Greg, Emma, Lilly and I will go to Hawaii the end of March. We'll have some spring visits from family. Greg and Emma are going to California tomorrow to see his sister and nephew there. We will talk, plan, laugh, think about our children, and get together with friends just as we always have done. I can't understand that it won't be like this forever. I wonder if anyone really can?

I ask myself if I am really in denial but I know there is no other way to be right now. Life just *IS*.

I have, at other times, looked at friends losing a loved one and wondered how they could seem so surprised or not aware of what seemed obvious to me from the outside looking in. Now I understand. We just can't take it all in, every waking moment. But the simple fact of this impending loss guides our every step.

Greg is taking care of details and it is satisfying to him. I am learning more about everything he has handled for us these years. But it still seems like a game and not real.

Some days I am worn out by living such tumult and uncertainty. I find my way through to another day and we keep going. I must narrow my world. It is hard but I just need *simple*. I need quiet and solace. My life is a confusing mix of realities.

We are held together by threads of love and friendship. I am in awe and wonder of it.

Remember what you love about those people next to you.

February 22

GREG'S CARINGBRIDGE LETTER

Four days now since I have had a "shift"...... tough, hard....hoping each morning to wake up feeling different, feeling better, even slightly better...the same....head fuzzy, left hand, side struggling to function. I make it work, fix my coffee....just now try to rub my left eye with my left hand....hard to find both..

am I scared? I don't think so.....sad, disappointed that it is coming faster than I thought it would. I want/need more time in better shape...back to surrender/acceptance. I am not going to give up "doing" things but I am going to ask for help and soon.....on lots of levels. I have to let go of life being even what it was last fall....the "new normal"....So I beg of the spirits to let me talk and think as long as possible ....please tumor stay away from the brain stem!!

Finish projects now!! Get help...don't alarm people...be honest...do what I can ... LIVE!!

February 26, 4 a.m.

GREG'S CARINGBRIDGE LETTER

Stumbling, hard to focus, one small fall, no balance, fuzzy brain....I am afraid. Life as I knew it is coming to a close, done, finis....even a wheel chair sounds good this morning! Do I know what is going on? No. I just know it is not right. I will try and stack branches for a burn pile, do a little work...so glad Lilly is here for the weekend, so glad Emma is here.

What next? Can't walk? Talk? I don't like this phase, can't see well. I don't even know wht my emotions are this morning. Among them a great sadness. How am I going to face each day? Where do I spend my time?

I try to think what is happening this AM is not real but it is SO real, every movement, every breath....can a body shut down quickly?

February 27

GREG'S CARINGBRIDGE LETTER

Dr. Chamberlain's read of my MRI on Feb 1st...."The tumor is progressing. Do what you want to do now." Already 26 days have gone by!

What does that really mean to me?

Physically, it is harder to walk, I lean more to the left (I'd rather be left leaning than right!!), I am careful not to fall, I go for comfort....for example, this morning I sit in front of the fire drinking perked coffee (love the sound and smell), write in my journal at 3 am (steroid sleep/wake cycle), eating "poor man's cereal" – Peanut butter slathered between shredded wheat halves, heated and dosed with milk and a fair bit of sugar...with 5 kids, Mom could get us off to school stomachs filled with some protein cheaply and easily...try it, you might like it.

I can still write pretty easily with my right hand but it is hard to read what I have written (cataracts caused by steroids). With the increase in steroids, my skin is fragile again and barely a scratch makes me bleed. As a family, we have decided to try this increase to give me some quality of life. It seems to help a bit.

Today I had to grab a bandaid which happened to be a Barbie bandaid and it reminded me of our parenting days (Do we allow Barbies or not was always the challenging question!) "Srider" flat footed Barbies became the compromise. I remember a day when I told Lilly I would play whatever she wanted for a few hours and there I was playing Barbies!!

Back to tumor land, a metaphor that came to me yesterday is that I have been in a very sweet room filled with friends, food, laughter and travel (virtual and real) when hiding outside the door lurks this mass of black "gak" (a slimy goo we used to make for our kids)...it is starting to creep in through the cracks and come toward me. This is a battle that I cannot win- the big question is how long can I hold it off?

I need more help and friends are stepping up to the plate in amazing ways....transcribing stories, helping organize and sort through a lifetime of photos and papers, helping with Platinum printing....it is not easy to surrender to this beast. I do hate this tumor and what it has robbed from me.

CHAPTER 20

MARCH 2012

*It would not be much of a universe if it wasn't
home to the people you love.*

—Stephen Hawking

March 2

GREG'S CARINGBRIDGE LETTER

To My Brain Tumor-

Ok, I get it, you are there and you're not going away. You have chosen only brains to be your family. The truth is I hate you. You are not welcome. We have had a rocky relationship for 17 months. I have done everything in my power, with an army of supporters, but to no avail. I am holding up a white flag- I surrender to this powerful GBM beast. I turn over my chemicals, my turkey tail mushrooms, all my weapons but I don't give you my spirit. I will live beyond you, so in the end you may take my body but not my soul/spirit/my life force!

In our peace treaty I ask for a few things, then I will go with you peacefully. And just so you know, there will be many people helping me go...I hope you don't mind crowds! You will have to deal with anger and tears because you are not popular on our island.

My demands:

Allow me to have one week on the beach with Lilly, Emma and Nancy in Hawaii at the end of March. I want to be able to walk comfortably.

Allow me to stay in reasonably good condition so my daughter, Clara, can feel comfortable staying in Spain, Lilly can stay in school, and I get to Emma's graduation. That gives you two deadlines, end of April and first of June.

The next one might be a stretch for you but there is no real rush you know- I want mobility and clear thinking until August. That would give me a wedding, a boat trip and the biggest margarita bash ever for Nancy's 62nd birthday.....the return of Janis Joplin....I envision an outdoor concert by my amazing wife! Mark that date, August 18th.

So big BT, I think my demands are fair- I really don't know how much compassion you have. (I assume very little because your reputation is not good, I need to say)....but can we sit at the table and negotiate? Just remember, I am giving you my life and you are only getting a body.

March 2

NANCY'S CARINGBRIDGE LETTER

Now, a week later, life has taken on an intensity that sharply calls my attention all the time. Greg's shift is physical but also internal. He can't sleep because of the steroids so he wakes up very early. This early time, for him, has been a time of deep searching, mourning and traveling down his path. I wake up a few hours later and we have our precious, uninterrupted time to talk.

While we, together, feel our losses deeply, I also see his path diverging from mine in ways. That part is sad beyond words and incomprehensible. We talk calmly about a time when he will no longer be with us. How can we talk about it matter-of-factly? I suppose it is because we are still sharing the loss and that makes it easier to bear, for now and just for now.

It frightens me when I try to imagine how I will live without Greg who knows my deepest fears, hopes, dreams, and laughter. He is my best friend and beloved companion. I do not want to take a moment for granted. I am allowing myself to just indulge in the simplicity of focusing on Greg and the girls right now. I feel badly that I am not a very good friend to others but I know that this is how and where I need to be.

I also need an amazing amount of time alone right now. I have so much to try to process. I wonder mostly: wonder and wander. I take long walks in the woods with only the company of my dearest dog companion, Phoebe. It is a great comfort to me. I am an earth- connected person and grateful to live somewhere that this is possible. The rich, dark earth, green moss and baby nettles are all my companions. Even the slimy mud is a welcome friend to me.

Despite this shift that we have both spoken of, Greg is still very much *in* this world. He has his friends whom he puts to work on unending projects, he is still telling his stories and they are being transcribed, and today he was overseeing our rain water system upgrade and calling to get new gravel for the drive way...and then played table tennis! That's our Greg!!

We had our first visit from Hospice today. It was an informational visit because they cannot work with us while Greg is still having treatments. But they left us feeling confident that we will be well guided and taken care of when we are ready to end treatment. I am relieved because I have found myself surprised more than once by disappointing experiences with medical personnel and have become a bit jaded.

We wait and wonder what will come and when. Meanwhile we live each minute in a new way. It helps to look forward to Hawaii later in March.

Our friends who are our angels feed us: with food, spirit, laughter and endless love. Of my many wonderings, the "how and why" that our family is the focus of so much love is still at the top. I know I may never really understand that, but I completely understand the power of this much love.

March 15

GREG'S CARINGBRIDGE LETTER

It is getting harder to walk, move-starting to use a walker around the house. Right hand still good, brain working, balance off....We are using steroids to maintain quality of life (standard procedure with GBM end stage...reduces swelling) No idea how long this could go on. It is challenging to say the least~for all of us. Crazy to be in this state of reasonable functioning knowing I could be gone in the near future! What is the near future?

Nancy and I are heading to Harrison Hot Springs for a romantic getaway today for a few days.....then Hawaii for a week with Emma and Lilly for important family time AND warm water. In the next week or two we should know a little more~~how aggressive this BT will be and how much benefit the higher steroid will give me.

My spirit? I would not say dancing, more dragging. I love this world, I want to stay longer and as I wrote once, I will LIVE until I die. This, I think, will be the hardest transition for me- from mobile to immobile.

I am very peaceful these days ~ comforted by the love and support that surrounds me. Highlight of the last two weeks was camping and rowing my Chamberlain Gunning Dory.

March 16

GREG'S CARINGBRIDGE LETTER

Harrison Hot Springs~the perfect spot, perfect timing, totally relaxing. We went to the Copper room for dinner and had prime rib and seafood. We danced to Neil Young's Harvest Moon played by the "Jones Boys" with a very happy, enthusiastic drummer. (we have seen them here before on other trips). We can still dance without falling in a heap even though we do more left turns than right. So thankful for our time together.

I am now using a walker to get around. I think it helps Nancy not worry as much but a very hard transition and the beginning of many other adjustments that I don't look forward to. I decorated my walker with reflectors, a bicycle bell (it is loud), and an led headlight. I was up at 5 this morning sitting by the fire in the big lounge here. There was supposedly no coffee till 7 but the manager came by and brought me a perfect cup of coffee so I could sit by the fire and write my morning journal entry.

The changes the last couple of days have been huge. I am losing mobility faster than I could have imagined. It seems like there is no reason to this madness. Hoping things can stabilize enough for the next 10 days so I can go to Hawaii with Nancy, Emma and Lilly without problems.

March 16

NANCY'S CARINGBRIDGE LETTER

It occurred to me tonight, as I watched many older couples here dancing, that Greg and I are deeply blessed to have found each other and had our twenty-three years of marriage. It is a crazy, miraculous and glorious experience to share this kind of intimacy. I am ever so grateful, and yet, as I watch these couples in their eighties dancing, I feel so sad and cheated that we will not be able to grow old together. We have always had so much fun, so I know we would be out there dancing in 20 years and, who knows what else?

In some ways, it seems like we have packed in our future in these last 17 months. We have tried to do have every adventure we might have had over a longer period. It feels bittersweet tonight. There will never be enough time.

March 17

NANCY'S JOURNAL

Harrison Hot springs, early morning...I can't sleep. I have been awake for hours worrying. Greg gets up, falls, pees in his pants, gets himself up and back to bed but I can't sleep. I am worried about going to Hawaii and about Clara. Greg is losing mobility and I worry about taking on more than I can manage.

I *hate* having to make these decisions on my own with no roadmap. What about Lilly and school? And what about these nights?

I am tired in body and spirit. Tired of handling everything and tired of the weight of the world.

March 19

NANCY'S CARINGBRIDGE LETTER

I just put on a special pair of earrings that I bought in Paris on a special day in 2003 when I was with Lilly on her 11th birthday. I remember trying to decide if I really could buy them. I bet they only cost $10.00, but it was a big decision at the time. Now they always bring back a memory of that precious day.

Friday night we watched Warhorse filmed in Dartmoor National Park, close to our home in England and a place we dearly loved. Seeing it on film washed us in happy memories.

I am struck by how we have moments in time, moments that stay with us, when we never knew what was ahead. Later, we embrace these moments as part of our story. Today our big questions continue to be asked.

March 20

NANCY'S CARINGBRIDGE LETTER

How many words are there for "roller coaster"? Clearly, not enough for me to adequately describe this experience. The cars on the roller coaster have slowed down in the track in the last couple of days.

Once again, an increase in steroids has proven to give Greg a leap in functioning that feels great. His walking is steadier and the walker is now gathering dust. He had a pretty good day yesterday and a great day today. He keeps saying he is using table tennis as his gauge of how he is doing. He is not only still in the game but still winning it!!

Fingers crossed, we will be on the warm beaches in a few days.

March 25

NANCY'S CARINGBRIDGE LETTER

All is well here with us on Maui. We have a nice, comfy condo right on the beach. We hear the ocean waves all the time. In fact, right now I am sitting by the open door with a slight breeze and listening to the sound of crashing waves.

It is all quite easy. Greg can sleep as much as he wants to and also can easily get on the beach. Today he floated in the water too. The girls are having a great time. We all four appreciate the break from making major decisions and worrying about what is around the next corner. Now we make decisions like, "Should I put on SPF 15 or 30?" We rented snorkel gear and we can see so much right off our beach!

The tumor is definitely making its presence known and we can use the steroids to give Greg a bit more mobility, but it is erratic and parts of the day seem better than others. The walker and cane are essential now for safety.

It is delightful to see big smiles on Emma and Lilly's faces as they sit in the sun and negotiate how to get the best tan. They have stepped up to the plate without question, and help Greg with whatever he needs. Lilly has decided not to go back to school after this spring break so she can spend time with her Dad and help at home. It was an arduous but good decision and feels like a relief.

While it is heavenly to have this time out of time, reality continues to creep in. As we look ahead, we know days together are limited. We will continue to carve out our time together as a family knowing that our family time is what we need the most. Unfortunately, it won't always include 80 degree temps, swimmable ocean waves, and humpback whales.

March 26

NANCY'S CARINGBRIDGE LETTER

We talked with Clara in Spain today and we have decided that she will come home early. It is a relief to have made a decision and *very* sad at the same time. We are not sad that she will be home, but sad for the "why" she will be home. She is not ready to leave but feels like it is what she needs to do.

We all cried a bit today: Greg cried when he received a beautiful email note that reflected so well who he is in this world. We cry over losing him. How can it be?

As much fun and relaxing as it is to be here, Greg still has this f****** tumor and it is doing what it's goal is to do – to his body, not to his soul. It is hard to put these facts together as I gaze out over the beautiful blue water, the contours of the other islands, the green grass and palms and think of this deep sadness in our lives.

We need each other and we need unlimited and uninterrupted access to each other now. We are grateful to have this time.

CHAPTER 21

APRIL 2012

Before you know kindness as the
deepest thing inside,
you must know sorrow as the
other deepest thing.
You must wake up with sorrow.
. . . Then it is only kindness that
makes sense anymore . . .

—Naomi Shihab Nye, "Kindness"

April 1

NANCY'S CARINGBRIDGE LETTER

The days are not easy for Greg and each day may be different than the last or the next. The same goes for each hour.

The calm and glorious sunny day today was good medicine and the food brought to us is nurturing and nourishing. The flowers in our house are lovely and fragrant.

Lilly and Emma are here and always at the ready. They are both devoted and loving. Greg does not feel comfortable to be left at home alone anymore, so it is helpful to have more hands. Clara will be home a week from today. It will take some time for her to adjust and I feel for her. Greg and I will be leaning on the three of them a lot. They bring so many gifts and I feel a bit like a mother duck who has a need to fluff up my feathers and gather them all near.

We have a Hospice visit tomorrow and are trying to decide if more Avastin treatments are worth it. We will not have any Hospice services unless Greg discontinues this treatment. The decision feels weighty.

I spent the whole afternoon outside digging dirt and weeding. It was great. We both sat out on the deck in the sun.

April 2

NANCY'S JOURNAL

It is a better day today. Adjusting medications seem to be helping. We had a good visit with Hospice nurse today. Greg seems clear on no more Avastin.

He is going over to a friend's later to watch some B-ball playoffs and I am off for a walk.

April 4

GREG'S CARINGBRIDGE LETTER

Last journal entry from Greg. Nancy will continue updates of my condition.

I am now 19 months out from my initial diagnosis of brain tumor (GBM). Ole BT has now clearly worked into my head. The metaphor I have is that he is at a control panel with valves controlling specific parts of my body, my left motor control, my eyesight, my fine motor dexterity, balance, leg strength, energy, speech and emotions. It feels like BT is starting to slowly, slowly shut down the valves of each function.

He plays an evil game of loosening one up for a while, giving me a short reprieve before shutting it down again. I do not know which is the last valve he will turn down. I am diving into my inner spiritual world these days being guided by my wind spirit that has blown me so sweetly on my path of life until a harsh gust slammed BT into my body.

My earth spirit is pulsating through my body comforting me as I deal with winds of change. I have never experienced such deep sadness. So deep and never ending.....a never ending crevasse of sadness. I love this world so much and I do not want to give it up.

Tears welled up and overflowed this last week from the depths of this sadness. Unending tears. A question arises within me as a visual person. I wonder where all of those many beautiful images of the world that I carry with me will go? Do I take them with me or are they released into the world somehow?

So as my body shuts down it becomes my journey to walk alone.....to leave peacefully a life that I love, people I love, a world that I love.... I feel complete. I know I gave love to this world.

My vision of passing from life to death is one of my riding on the back of a grizzly bear softly padding toward the gossamer veil that separates life and death. And when we get to the veil the grizz will gently set me down on the other side.

I do not know what will be there but I know it will be peaceful and I will be OK.....more than OK....what will I be? Content? As the grizz sets me down I will feel all of your love and support behind me. Thank you for that. The grizz will quietly leave me and find another to help with *their transition. My wind and earth spirit will follow me through to the other side.*

You can honor me and celebrate my life by saying "yes" to whatever comes your way. Love those around you. Speak from your heart. Say what you really think, honor yourself and Love, Love, Love.

April 6

NANCY'S CARINGBRIDGE LETTER

I read and re-read every email message, card or letter to Greg. He asks several times a day if there are more. Wisdom, love and compassion shine through in all of these communications and grace us. Each individual expression is a gift, whether it is profound and wise, a funny blip, or a memory. It all mixes together to create the beautiful web of love that comforts us.

Our Hospice nurse told us today that he has never seen anyone with as much support as we have. It is stunning. Every piece fits in to make it all work. Sometimes distant support and love, a candle lit, a prayer, even when you think we are not aware of it, is the greatest gift. It all matters.

It is chaotic around here without many moments of quiet. We need them. Lilly and Emma have taken off to pick up their cousin and her fiancé who will be here this weekend. Tomorrow I will go off to pick up Clara. Daily, we must readjust to new routines to accommodate Greg's physical state. Sometimes he has more strength than other times so it is difficult to predict.

Personal visits are difficult because it is harder and harder for Greg to talk. Handwriting is not working any more either. I type for him and he is making phone calls as he can. We are all grappling with the sad truth that *none* of us has enough time with Greg.

Life still happens. The vacuum cleaner and the dishwasher break, the door to Emma's cabin got stuck today with her inside, bills have to be paid, dishes washed, compost emptied, financial aid forms submitted, laundry done but never put away and all of this happening while we want and need to just process with each other.

We are stunned, scared, very sad and working hard to keep ourselves together.

Gracious night helpers are allowing the girls and me to sleep. I resist every step of help but then I am so grateful for it. The tide is rolling out and we can't catch it.

Thank God for the sun today and for daffodils, flowering cherry trees, plum trees and hyacinths. For yellow labs and angels who come disguised as human beings. Oh yes, and for Hospice.

April 7

NANCY'S CARINGBRIDGE

Waiting for Clara's plane. I cannot wait to see her and I also worry about how coming home will be for her. My heart aches as I anticipate her experience. Being away from home for even just one day has been difficult for me. Every day for Greg is a new decline and I grieve each lost moment.

I wailed in the car today like I never have before. I understand the "Wailing Wall" now.

My grief came from a deep well of sadness that was new

territory even after all of this time of loss. It was primal. I know it was good for me.

Thankfully, I could still drive while crying.

Greg fulfilled his dream to get his niece Sarah and her husband out to James Island today. He had a lot of help and needed it, but he made it happen and it meant the world to him. I am quite sure there are stories to be told for a long time!

Tomorrow we will go to our traditional Easter gathering with our dearest our islandian friends. Greg will be transported in a tractor since it is a hike up to a beautiful moss-covered hill over-looking Hunter Bay. He would never consider missing this occasion, no matter what it takes to get there.

April 11

NANCY'S CARINGBRIDGE LETTER

Clara is adjusting amazingly well. All three girls are amazing. I am so thankful for them. With all four of us working hard, it still takes all day to get the simplest of tasks done. I don't know how we could do without them. We are talking, crying and holding each other. I am grateful for this precious time with the five of us, just to move in and out of conversations and process. We can't deny the obvious as much as we would like to.

We are listening closely to what Greg needs. His needs come before us all right now. Some days are better than others. Today is not one of those better days.

April 11

CaringBridge Letter
from the Care Committee

Our always-reaching-out Greg is now going into an inward time as he continues his personal journey. Clara has returned from Spain, so the whole family is here to walk these new steps together. He is working hard on his process and it feels good to him to have his family around him. They are especially appreciating this time – sharing laughter and tears.

Greg's situation is up and down, so he is calling the shots. He wants to be the initiator of any contact with people rather than having it come from the other direction. His family is following Greg's lead in how he wants to spend his remaining energy and spirit.

He is still directing a few projects around their home and working on a photography show in May. That is really all he has energy for. He is sleeping a lot and will be doing more. There are times when he is able to contact people to say goodbye. He has been and will do that as he can. It is an emotionally wrenching experience for him. This, of course, is a time to do only and whatever HE wants to do. Mostly this is being with Nancy and the girls. What WE all can do is to grant them that sacred space to share Greg's remaining days.

With grateful thanks for all your love.

April 16

NANCY'S CARINGBRIDGE LETTER

Greg has had a couple of good days! His functioning has improved, he is steadier on his feet and his mind is clear. He is thrilled with this upswing and taking full advantage, as is his way.

Greg's sister and brother in law came for the weekend and between Greg's energy and their desire to help us in *every* way possible, it was a whirlwind and great fun.

But then there are those goodbyes, which are so hard.

April 22

GREG'S CARINGBRIDGE LETTER, TRANSCRIBED BY NANCY

It feels like I am going into the sleeping stage of the GBM....my body shutting down, I am weaker, sleeping more. I can use the walker some around the house but I appreciate having the wheelchair more often. I don't think I realized how weak a body could become. Talking is more difficult. I appreciate all of your thoughts even though I will not be able to respond or have visitors any more. The good part is that there is very little pain and I am able to sleep comfortably. I have a cot outside on the deck so on many of these clear nights with sweet air, I sleep much of the night outside.

Our male friends take turns spending the night with me so Nancy can get a full night's sleep and are willing to spend the night outside with me which is most appreciated.

We just added a photo of the poster advertising my first solo photog-

raphy exhibition. Preparing for it is keeping me alive and my mind active. Here is my photography bio that goes with the poster:

In 1961, I was 12 years old my father, grandfather, brother and I took a trip to Glacier National Park. With me was my trusty little Brownie Box camera. I shot a few rolls of 127 color film. When we came home to East Lansing, Michigan, I dropped the film off at the drug store, returning a week later for the prints. I entered some of the prints in the local youth talent show and got an Honorable Mention. Although it was barely a step above a "participant" ribbon it was enough to inspire me to think I was a real photographer.

Six years later I graduated from my Brownie Box camera to my first 35 mm film camera. At the time there was a 24" snow storm in East Lansing and I went out to photograph it not knowing how difficult photographing snow with black and white film really is. A friend had a dark room so we developed the film and two of those photographs are on display here.

When I put that blank piece of paper into the developing chemicals and a picture appeared I was hooked for life on the magic of a dark room. I graduated from high school in 1967 and went to the University of Washington in to study architecture. I soon found that in the basement of the Architecture building was an amazing dark room run by an old German photographer named, Christian Staub, who had worked with many of the well known European photographers in the early 50s. He took me under his wing and I became his lab assistant.

I spent the next 3-4 years working in the dark room, learning from a real master. At that time, I tried to turn any writing assignment into a photography assignment enabling me to spend hours in the dark room. At one point I was shooting 3-4 rolls of film a week. This included studio work and work with a 4X5 view camera. Like many students at the time

I bought my first Pentex Spotmatic-two 35 mm camera. Zoom lenses were not high quality back then so the Pentax crowd would buy fixed lenses from pushy salesmen at Forty Seventh Street Photo in New York. My two favorite lenses were 24mm wide angle and a 105 mm portrait lens.

After graduating from UW, I got my first medium format camera, a Mimaya C 220 and fell in love with the larger negatives because of the incredible detail they could capture. Like many back then, we thought we could become professional photographers, sell our work and make a living being photographers. I joined an arts community in 1975 and became the photographer of the community.

At this time in my life, I fell in love with backpacking and started using slide film. I now have a collection of thousands of slides from the trips I took.

My photography became a side hobby when I moved to our island to teach, got married, built a house and had three kids. I found little time to pursue the photography that I loved.

In the mid-1990s I was asked to help with a photography class at the high school so I once again had access to a dark room. About this time Lorrie Harrison and I started collaboration on the book Kindred Spirits. My C220 got dusted off and I once again began to do dark room work.

After Kindred Spirits was published, I was recognized as a photographer again. I became a photography teacher at our island Middle/High school entering the world of the digital camera. Presently I am using a Nikon D50 and a Canon G9 for my work.

The work in this show includes work from as early as 1968 as well as more recent images.

I am grateful to photography for keeping my eyes wide open.

Although I have captured many images with a camera, there are so many more in my mind's eye that are unrecorded. As my life comes to a close, I wonder where all of those images go?

April 22

NANCY'S CARINGBRIDGE LETTER

Our days are somewhat varied according to Greg's functioning which completely unpredictable, even within the day. This means his caregiving needs are in constant flux. He spends some active time each day up and around and some days he probably does not rest enough!

For safety, we can't leave him alone anymore and he needs more care and attention all the time. As a family, we are grateful that, with a *lot* of help and support, we can manage it ourselves. For us, this is the way it should be and we want to be here and make the end of his life as full of love and joy as we can. My deepest respect goes to all who give to us so selflessly so that we can do this as a family.

We are very busy while all the while the girls are carrying on their lives as much as possible. They all contribute to the workload as they can. I marvel at my wise young women and I know that this time is a gift for them that will live on throughout their lives. I would be *so lost* without them.

The other nights, as Greg mentioned, we have one of his male buddies here – it is a godsend. In addition to helping Greg, they are saving my sanity. As one of my children pointed out yesterday, "If Mama ain't happy..."

We had a couple of guys over yesterday to help with major

gardening projects. Greg was outside the entire time consulting and directing. It feels good and vital to have vegetables planted and growing, maybe it symbolizes the cycle of life to me. Whatever it is, it adds an important dimension. My soul is comforted by my surroundings: the green, the earth, the birds, the quiet.

Our care committee meets with us once a week and serves us in every way in between. They are wise and unwavering in their affirmation and grounding for us. It is hard to put words for this kind of love.

We relish each precious day. I am grateful for our beautiful hand built home and the well-tended five acres we are part of here. We have much to lean on and breathe into. We have more than most and it is a deep and precious gift. We know we are held closely by so many every day. Sometimes in the frantic parts of the day, I forget to be grateful. Writing this helps me remember.

April 25

GREG'S CARINGBRIDGE LETTER, TRANSCRIBED BY NANCY

This morning I woke feeling BT slowly turning the sleeping valve up. More and more, my body feels like going to sleep. It is getting harder and harder to stay awake. I will be sleeping outside in "Camp BT" until I take my last breath sweet SW breeze coming all the way from Maui. While lying on the beach in Maui, the perfect breeze wafted over me, the perfect temperature to a micro degree went through my body and I absorbed it into every cell. Now I lie on my cot in Camp BT and the same sweet breeze comes over me from across the ocean, the olympic beaches on which I spent so much time, over Mt. Olympus where Steve Adams and I climbed, over blue glacier, over the old port city of Pt. Townsend, across the straits, over Iceberg point, over waters and forests of our island and finally to me. I breathe that air and take it into every cell of my body.

This is where I need your help. There are some important things coming up....Lilly's birthday is Saturday, Emma's is a week later, my photography show a few days after that, Mother's day, then Clara's birthday May 20th. If at all possible I need to be breathing through Memorial Day weekend for Clara to go to her long awaited trip to her first music festival, Sasquatch. Please breathe with me, help me stay alive so I can share these times with the people I love. I need your collective energy to ask the spirits to keep my alive and breathing for these important passages.

The photo show is ready to hang thanks to the efforts of my Platinum Angels. They have worked tirelessly to make beautiful prints from my images. This photo show, which has kept me going, would not have happened without their continued and dogged efforts.

When BT makes the last turn of the valve, and I take my last breath and climb on the back of the grizzly, I envision my four women, Nancy, Emma, Lilly and Clara gathered around me helping me climb on her back as I go. I know they will be with me.

April 27

NANCY'S CARINGBRIDGE LETTER

We have had some sweet family time this week. I can't think of anything more calming and healing for us than to just be together as we have. Tonight, the five of us lay in bed together and the girls and I sang to Greg for an hour and a half! We sang just about every song we knew and some we did not know, from old lullabies to campfire songs. Greg kept saying, "Your voices sound so beautiful." I kept thinking, "Wow, his hearing really *is* bad!"

What we lacked in skill we made up for in pure love and it was one of the nicest evenings I have ever spent.

We have also had some good laughs this week, resulting in my learning how to load a YouTube video of Greg teaching Emma's friend how to make his family's delicacy: a shredded wheat split in half and spread with peanut butter, doused with half and half and warmed in the microwave. It looks as awful as it sounds.

CHAPTER 22

MAY 2012

When despair for the world grows in me
and I wake in the night at the least sound . . .
I come to the presence of still water.
. . . I rest in the grace of the world, and am free.

—Wendell Berry, "The Peace of Wild Things"

May 5

GREG'S CARINGBRIDGE LETTER

Lying outside waiting for the super moon to rise, tucked in by my sweet wife (everyone should be tucked in at night), under quilts and my sleeping bag, warm and cozy, still alive, still fighting to be alive, feeling the tumor trying to put me to sleep. Each minute is valuable now. Simply talking exhausts me so I am conserving as much energy as I can to stay alive as long as I can. My girls rally around me. Our home feels really sweet to me right now. As a family we are learning about dying. Thank you for breathing with me.

May 5

NANCY'S JOURNAL

I have had so little time to write or reflect these days. I just go, go, go all day, either taking care of Greg or doing constant dishes and housework, scheduling, answering the phone and talking with the girls. There is so little time to be in my own head and I wonder what is even in there now?

So much of the time I don't even let myself feel this loss. Greg and I are on such different trajectories now. His is all about going and yet staying as long as he can. All of his energy goes into just that – maintaining, seeing a few people and saying good byes. He is living for his photography show.

Mine is all about keeping him alive and taking care of him and not much else. I have some vague idea that I have a future but it is overwhelming. I can't imagine it because imagining it means no Greg so how can I do that?

May 8

NANCY'S JOURNAL

Can anyone live with these ups and downs and constant changes and not lose their mind? I wonder. I can't count on anything. Now Greg is feeling better, not physically, but mentally. He is full of energy and excitement and this gives him stamina, which changes the ball game again. I don't feel like we are in constant crisis. He is not so needy every minute so I can relax a bit. Then I think, "Was I overreacting?"

May 12

NANCY'S CARINGBRIDGE LETTER

The photography opening is over. It was a *great* event and Greg was present and enjoyed all of it.

Now we are in the "next phase," whatever that may be. And that *whatever* is a huge word for us now. One minute is different from the next.

There are a few consistencies: Greg's physical functioning is slowly weakening. He spends more time in bed and when he is up, he uses the wheelchair exclusively. He is alert and so himself: alive, engaged, dreaming about adventures. How fortunate he is to have his mind. With the excellent advice from our Hospice nurses, we are learning some medication management techniques that enhance Greg's quality of life even if his body is not cooperating.

He sleeps off and on but when he is not sleeping he likes listening to music and podcasts on his iPad. We have a double bed downstairs with windows all around where he spends his time. It looks out over the grass and woods with a view of the white lilac that is blooming now. Being downstairs, with the open living design of our house, allows Greg to be a part of whatever any of us are doing in our busy household.

There is also a nice bed outside on the deck now. It has taken the place of the cot for "camp BT." A friend built it and it is comfortable, with a back that can be raised. Greg is out there right now enjoying the beautiful, warm day. As frustrating as it is for him to not be able to use his body, his ability to "roll with the punches" has not diminished. He has the most incredible attitude. He keeps us laughing and having fun.

Greg requires full-time assistance for everything now. The girls are learning to manage their lives so they can still have fun out and about and help at home. It is not easy but they are doing it wisely and with great sensitivity to the needs of their mom and dad. We would not be able to do it without them. For me, there is so much to be said for sharing this experience with them. As a family, our world and our experience of losing Greg is unique and it is a bonding experience to walk through it and find our way together – or to feel lost together.

Our care team is invaluable, pitching in with love and support. I don't know how we would function without every helping hand. Apparently, we have made a name for ourselves at our local Hospice from the mainland for the amount of support we have from our community.

There is so much to this experience that no one can help us with, however. It is complicated to navigate the shores of long-term caregiving and what it means. Greg and I have the gift of being here together and being able to have this phase of our lives in our own home with our family. That is a lasting and deeply rewarding gift.

Other aspects are more bewildering. While we do have each other now, each day we face losing more while we live with constant uncertainty. There is that blessing of learning to "live in the moment" but the experience of literally knowing that everything can change in a heartbeat, while working like crazy to maintain the now, is not ideal!

I think about my experience at other times of life when I have worked hard for something... climbing a mountain, getting a degree, giving birth, raising children. There is always that natural feeling of "When this is over I will have achieved something!" Or that "looking forward to the satisfaction of a job well done." With this experience, I am working hard all the time and when it is over? It goes without saying – more loss.

How does one make sense of that? I have been struggling with this concept for a few weeks. Someone sent an article entitled "New Grief" which is about how with the advancement of modern medicine, our culture's view of death and grieving is changing both for the person with a terminal illness and their caregivers.

One life ends when you hear "terminal diagnosis" and another begins. There is an entire new life to be lived between diagnosis and eventual death and none of us are prepared for it. Each step is new and completely unfamiliar territory for which we have had no preparation, and rarely have a model to follow. In this new phase, we don't get to plan or dream. We sometimes feel a little hopeful and we feel foolish or "negative" when things seem better than we expected. We live with a lot of anxiety. Reading the article was as though someone had walked into my life and illuminated it.

May 17

NANCY'S CARINGBRIDGE LETTER

Greg wanted to have one more night sleeping in a tent by the water. It felt daunting to the girls and me but we called his faithful friends and guess what? Before we knew it, we were in a friend's boat on our way to a Washington State Park Island. It was not an easy feat to get Greg into the boat but with the willing hands, hearts and muscle of his friends, we did it. We had the most picture-perfect weather imaginable and a delightful evening. This park has wheelchair accessibility so with muscles provided by the guys, Greg got to tour around before the evening by the campfire.

He went to bed earlier than the rest of us. One by one, most wandered off to tents and sleeping bags. About eleven or so, there were a few diehards (including me) enjoying the campfire and talking while sipping a little whiskey. About the time that we were talking of giving it up and crawling into our tents, I got a page on the walkie talkie from Greg wanting to get up and join the action around the campfire...so, of course he did. He had his standard bowl of frosted flakes and half and half with his whiskey!! What a night.

We got a hospital bed this week in place of the full-sized bed. It is easier to maneuver and Greg can raise and lower it easily so he can eat and visit. The hummingbird feeder is outside one window and a bird feeder for the other birds by another window. It is sunny and bright.

Greg seems to be entering the phase of sleeping more. He wakes up just to eat and take a shower and have a visit or two. It is a bit depressing, but maybe things will improve...they sometimes have.

May 20

NANCY'S JOURNAL

Clara's seventeenth birthday is supposed to be a happy day. What a different life we lead now. It is hard to celebrate another birthday and I don't feel very celebratory. I am sure I will rally but now I am sad and tired. The camping trip was a blast and yesterday we had fun going out to breakfast and to the library to look at Greg's photos. But last night, when I ran to the store, I saw cars at the Community Center and realized there was a lovely concert going on – I am trapped here at home and missing out on so much.

The evenings are difficult. Greg is sad and we are both tired. Greg is harder and harder to move and lift. Sometimes we have time alone and we still have fun. Such a confusing existence. I still have him and then I don't. I am ready for my life to move on and yet I feel guilty saying that. It feels crazy because I want and need to savor every moment with Greg so nothing makes any sense.

The alternative to how we are living now is going through Greg's dying process and how can I want that? But sometimes I just want to fast forward.

I feel like I need a shot of wisdom about how to get through this. I can't exactly grieve any loss because the *BIG LOSS* is coming.

May 26

NANCY'S CARINGBRIDGE LETTER

Greg's status is up and down and unpredictable. He is failing physically at a slow and steady rate. He can do little for himself and now mostly stays in bed. But he sits up and is interested in visits when he has the energy. He continues with this schedule, waking up for a couple of hours in the middle of the night, but stays in his wheelchair rather than trying to use the walker and risking a fall. Transfers are difficult – he has little strength to assist.

By evening, he feels down and discouraged. It is hard to watch him struggle so. I often go to bed sad and wondering what to expect in the morning. Consistently, however, he is perked up and feels good by morning. He has rich conversation with his "night friends," and he wakes up feeling good. The day goes downhill after a couple of hours. Talking takes so much effort – a visit or phone call can be exhausting.

Mentally, he is clear sometimes and other times not. He needs many reminders about his schedule. Fortunately, he is not in any pain.

But Greg, the dreamer, has not given up his dreams. Last week's idea was a plan to take a family trip to Greece. He had a great time fantasizing about it but had some trouble convincing the rest of us to buy the tickets.

Yesterday I had a 24-hour retreat at a cabin on our island. It was heavenly. I took a long walk and got dinner from a local take out. Then I slept 12 hours. It is difficult for me to realize how exhausted I really am.

Lilly took Greg out this morning for a bakery treat and drove to the beach with him. It is difficult for only one person to transfer him in and out of the car now but they managed and Greg enjoyed seeing some different scenery.

Tomorrow we have a bath aid coming from Hospice because we can no longer get him in our bath/shower set up. She will teach us to give bed baths and will come twice a week.

May 28

GREG'S CARINGBRIDGE LETTER, TRANSCRIBED BY NANCY

Through the yeoman efforts of my airplane buddies, Charlie Walker flew me around the San Juan Islands for one last plane ride on Sunday. At one point he turned the controls over to me and what great fun to be able to fly again with competence. Thanks to another pilot we were able to fly in a Cessna 182. It is a smooth plane to fly and there was room for Lilly to join us in the back seat. We circumvented the San Juan Islands and I got to look at the many islands I have camped on over the years. I am so thankful to have lived in the San Juan's for over 20 years now. I think it is one of the more beautiful places on earth. How fortunate I have been to be able to purchase land here. As I lay bedridden with a brain tumor pressing harder and harder, I delight in the hand crafted space wondering how Nancy and I had the time and energy in our lives to work full time, build a house, raise three kids and survive and enjoy it all.

May 27

NANCY'S JOURNAL

A nice quiet morning. I feel relieved to not have to torture myself with decisions and "what ifs" with the girls, grateful that all of that is settled and we can just be in each day. How many more there will be?

It is hard to say no to Greg, but I can't get him outside by myself any more. He should be able to have what he needs now, and that is the premise from which we are all operating. But when it conflicts with what's best for me, I have to say no.

It is very hard to do.

May 28

NANCY'S JOURNAL

I went to Pilates this morning and a friend came over to visit but stayed way too long after I got home so by the time she left, Greg was exhausted. It is hard when other people get the best of him. I feel guilty that it is hard to share him but I realize I have had to share him for our whole marriage because he is so public. Now I don't want to any more. I wonder if other people feel this way or is it just some strange quirk of mine?

May 31

NANCY'S JOURNAL

Greg's moods are so up and down. He is much more demanding and controlling and acts like no one knows how to do anything right except him. He gets obsessed with a certain idea or thought, like he wants to set everything up his way before he goes. I have never seen him like this before. At first I thought it was funny, but now it is irritating and strange.

Tonight, we are having a graduation celebration for Emma. Many people are helping and it feels good to do something normal and fun.

CHAPTER 23

JUNE 2012

we can't cheat death but we can make it
work so hard
that when it does take
us

it will have known a victory just as
perfect as
ours.

—Charles Bukowski, "a song with no end"

June 1

NANCY'S JOURNAL

Last night was so much fun. Honestly, I just can't believe how people pitch in to make our lives work. Emma felt honored and Greg was able to be up for about three hours. There was lots of help for him that was great for me. Greg and I had time alone at home together yesterday too and that was fun.

I want to go for a walk but I have to arrange for someone to be here. I hardly even remember what it was like to just go do something. Did I ever really get to do that? Will I ever have a choice about my life again? I am anxiously awaiting the next phase of my life, which is all in the abstract. On the surface, it makes sense but in reality, it is crazy because of what that means. I wonder if we all feel that way? I think we do.

June 3

NANCY'S JOURNAL

It was such an awful and frustrating day. I have cried and cried and cried. Greg is no longer the person I married. He is so narcissistic now. He has these crazy ideas of things he wants to do and no sense of how they might impact others around him. His "last requests" just keep going and going and does he consider the cost of it all? I don't want him to know how much he has changed. What good would it do? It would just make him feel bad. His ability to engage in a reciprocal relationship is just about gone. I get so angry at him and then feel terrible...beyond terrible and I cry and cry. Then he tells me he still has quality of life because he can have conversations.

I am not sure that I have quality of life sometimes. All I do is take care of one person or another. It feels like everyone has needs and they all seem to come to me. Even people who care about Greg want to talk to me about their sadness and loss. I am carrying the world on my shoulders. I think about others who have to do this for a loved one for years. I wonder how long I can go on like this. I feel imprisoned in this life, suspended in time.

June 9

NANCY'S CARINGBRIDGE LETTER

It is difficult to write these messages lately. I have such strong conflicting emotions as well as exhaustion. The daily tasks are a lot to manage and unpredictable. The five of us living here together a huge gift, but it is also five people, each with her (and one his) own set of emotions and needs. And as everyone knows, we have the best community support one could dream of *but* I am beginning to understand that doing this job "well" does not change the outcome or the dynamics.

We still must go through it *all*. Some days that means we sit around with Greg on the bed and laugh and talk and share our lives, other days that means that we are all stretched, edgy and anxious about everything.

I have days in which I cry all day and other days when my life seems as normal as I have learned to define that word for now.

We have many willing hands and yet when someone asks me what I need, it is impossible for me to answer. I need a robot and a butler.

Although Greg is alive and engaged, we have lost all semblance of our former family life. It has been eked away little by little without our realizing the magnitude of the changes until we look back at a photo or talk about a memory and wham! Reality hits us in the face.

I no longer have an actively involved life partner. I have total responsibility for the family, home, finances and five acres, and I also have most of the responsibility for caring for Greg (although I have good solid help from the girls and the angelic "night guys.") Every stage of this part is unknown. I bumble along like an idiot a lot of the time.

As with just about any experience in life, our decision to care for Greg at home (not sure what else we would have done?) has the good and the bad. Sometimes I long for more "professional" help as I imagine one would have from a Hospice program in a city.

From our Hospice on the mainland, we have a weekly nurse visit for an hour and twice a week bath aide. In addition, we have our medical needs covered such as equipment and medication. But I still feel so lost, alone and confused by the difficulties we face that are not "typical". I have read so many books and then so often think, "no one *ever* mentions this." It is strange and unknown territory. I'm constantly aware that what we are going through can only be understood by someone who has walked in similar shoes.

We get cabin fever and want to be part of the world outside of our home but it is a lot of work and difficult on many levels. We try to get out when we can. Today is high school graduation and we have spent a bit of time and energy planning how to get Greg there comfortably and we think we have a plan that will ensure success. He swears he wants to go to the party afterwards, which is an outdoor gig, so my guess is, he will. Many of the graduates are our dearest friends who have spent countless hours in our home so we are grateful to be able to attend.

I barely have time to read emails, much less answer them. On occasion, I can manage a phone call but when I have a few minutes I just have to try to find some time alone to process. I can't really be an integral part of anything that at one time defined who I was in the world, and this is most difficult for me. I can't dream of the future or make any plans at all.

As for Greg's status? He spends most of his time in bed these days. Transfers to the wheelchair are possible but difficult. He has a few hours a day of being engaged and having good conversations but then he is exhausted. His two to three hours in the night with the "night guy" is rich time for him. He loves to use the time to talk, look at slides or whatever comes up.

Phone calls are rare but he tries. His voice is so soft that it is difficult to understand him on the phone. He is completely dependent on us and that is hard for him.

Despite it all, we have some fun. We take our dinner plates over to Greg's bed and watch the zillions of hummingbirds at the feeder. The other night we played a card game and tried to keep Greg from cheating.

His mind is still active and we know this is a blessing, but it also leads him to envision so many things he would still like to do and in his mind, they are all possible. This is probably the cruelest aspect of the disease for him. He has such a passion for being alive and dreaming.

June 20

NANCY'S CARINGBRIDGE LETTER

It is finally warm outside and feels like summer.

Greg continues his slow decline. The changes seem gradual to me, but I am here every day so to others changes are more noticeable. What has not changed is the unpredictability. In fact, it is difficult to even say anything about how Greg is feeling because in two hours it might be different. I am constantly second guessing even my own observations.

He is peaceful these days and we have been having fun talking, snuggling, and lately even watching a movie. Much of the time he sleeps, and a good bit of his awake time is taken up with bathing, changing, and trying to eat. I am continually amazed at how a day goes by and I can't figure out where the time went.

Talking tires Greg out, so although he likes to have visits, it is difficult to plan and execute. He would love to talk on the phone but his voice does not project enough and this is a cause of frustration.

The girls are in and out with jobs and various social activities. It is a struggle for them to balance their needs to just be normal and be out doing things, and being home to help and spend time with Greg. I think they do it well.

I still marvel at how suddenly these three former teenaged girls grew into such loving, compassionate, wise women, seemingly overnight.

Greg has the slide projector, scanner and a lifetime of slides and negatives that he goes through when he has the energy and expertise available. This has been an ongoing middle of the night project, as well, and it has been great for him. He enjoys it and feels productive.

His "up in the wheelchair" trips have been fewer and saved for important times. He went to the annual tap recital on Friday night and was up for a Father's Day dinner on Sunday. He talked a few strong young men who were here for Father's Day to carry him upstairs in his wheelchair so he could see Lilly's newly decorated bedroom. They also took him on a tour outside.

Tonight, we plan to go to a solstice celebration on our island. For these latest outings, we have had the generous offer of a wheelchair-accessible van that's been a godsend.

Life is surreal, I suppose, but we humans are incredibly adaptable. We are capable of living with paradoxical feelings and the expansiveness of this is a revelation to me. How can I feel such joy alongside such grief? How can I feel one day as though I cannot take another step and two days later experience such pleasure in the simplest of tasks?

I remain nourished and deeply grateful for the natural beauty everywhere around me here. My soul is fed by the quiet of my walks, the sun, the green, the rain, the wild roses blooming everywhere, the lettuce in my garden, and the hummingbirds right outside the window. The natural world is so full right now and enables me to find a strength I never knew I had. I am grateful for resilience and how we help each other find this power in ourselves.

I sometimes find some treasured time to lie beside Greg and listen to his breathing. It feels limitless. It is almost impossible to believe it is not.

I will take this day and absorb all that I can of Greg and our blessings.

June 23

NANCY'S JOURNAL

So strange that nothing can change in my outward circumstances but I can feel dramatically different from one day to the next. I feel calmer with Greg. I am still struggling to integrate other people into our experience.

We need the help and Greg needs the fresh faces. But it is all focused on him and even my own friends come to see him and rarely even ask me how I am – not to mention offering help to *me*. Most people stay too long, not knowing that their visits take up too much of Greg's limited energy and not enough is left for his family.

I have no life partner any more, no one to care about what is going on with *me*. I have forgotten what it was like. I can hardly remember what Greg was like. I don't think anyone can really know how exhausting it is and just endless.

CHAPTER 24

JULY 2012

So to you, Friend, I confide my secret:
to be a discoverer you hold close whatever
you find . . .
Then, secure in where you have been,
you turn to the open sea and let go.

—William Stafford, "Security"

July 2

NANCY'S CARINGBRIDGE LETTER

It has been a difficult day. In addition to a broken washing machine and limping dishwasher, Greg has been congested all week and because he is mostly in bed all the time, it has been difficult for him to cough it up.

Last night he choked, which really scared him. I called hospice and started him on a medication for the secretions but a side effect was pronounced confusion with hallucinations. The nurse said it could take all day to wear off.

He was out of his mind all day talking in gibberish. We could not understand most of what he said but he did not stop all day. I can't imagine having *that* much to say but he sure does! We all just hung out with him taking turns. We wheeled him outside for a while and our friend Eric came over and played guitar for him. Finally, by evening he was a bit clearer. We could feed him some tonight but he does not eat too much. We are all exhausted.

Earlier in the week Greg got out in our friend's W/C accessible van and visited a few spots in the village, which he enjoyed immensely. He grapples with a severe nerve pain in his leg so transferring him to a wheelchair is hard on him but he says it was worth it.

He wants to see the 4th of July parade but we shall see how realistic that is closer to the time. I am exhausted tonight. Tomorrow is another day.

It often feels so strange to think that there is a whole world going on outside of our little bubble. We are all sad to miss a family wedding this weekend in Michigan. I think of how many people spend their days in caregiving roles, many of whom have a more difficult situation than ours. It takes so much grace and grit and love, loving when it is so complicated.

Many of us in life are called to love in such painful and unpredictable circumstances.

We continue to find this love to take care of Greg and each other, because we are so loved by all of you. There is a strong power in the gift we share with each other.

July 5

NANCY'S JOURNAL

Greg was determined to go out to the July 4th gathering and with *lots* of help, he did. Although I never say anything about his condition without second guessing myself, I think his life is ebbing. He is confused and more blank.

I don't even know what he is thinking any more. He asked me to snuggle with him today and "get things straight" but then he was too confused to talk. I looked at a photo of us on the computer from some years ago. I have always loved that photo. In my head, I said, "My husband is dying." I have never said that before. Sweet beautiful man he was.

July 7

NANCY'S CARINGBRIDGE LETTER

It has been a long five days. Greg's body is failing and he is transitioning to another reality. He had a few more days of hallucinations/delusions which were very difficult. Thankfully, we have appropriate medications from Hospice which help, but it was hard on all of us.

The last few days he has been sleeping most of the time, sometimes confused but not always. He says he is happy. He went to a 4th of July BBQ, thanks to several good friends who made it possible. He seemed out of it but said he had a good time.

He has a lot of fluid in his chest and he cannot really cough it out. He has trouble swallowing too. The coughing is frustrating for him and tonight he said he is ready to give up.

215

He has a large pressure sore on his ankle and is on antibiotics for that. He watches movies sometimes and today a friend came and read to him which he loved. We climb in bed with him and snuggle.

He slept outside last night. He knows he is moving closer to dying but when asked, he says his life has quality. He told me yesterday that he wants to "practice" and when I asked him what that meant he told me he envisions going through a long tunnel and he wants me there when he begins that journey.

It was twenty-five years ago today that Greg and met. I spent most of yesterday crying. It is all so overwhelming. I hate it that this ever happened, I hate it that Greg has to live on in such a limited capacity, I hate needing so much help, I hate never having a moment to myself, I hate it that my children can't have a normal life now, and I resent this ugly disease.

Greg loves being cared for and has settled into it with amazing grace. But he is also confused and oblivious to the whole picture. I envy that oblivion.

I was with both of my parents when they died and have been a caregiver for several others who were dying but nothing, nothing has ever prepared me for this.

There is so much and so little that others can do for us. Often the greatest gift is just to be able to hear our experience and walk with us, while understanding that questions are hard to answer.

There are such kind tangible gifts: my weeded flower bed, the night guys, dinners, laundry, the 4:00 chore guys, the massage I had today, those who come and sit with Greg so I can walk for an hour, the berries. And then the intangible gifts: the affirmation and acknowledgment from others that we are walking a difficult, many-layered path that only we can walk.

The girls are weary. As Greg gets more confused, it becomes much harder for them and it is difficult for all of us to make sense of it.

July 11

Nancy's Journal

We are intermittently so tired of it all. Sometimes it's me, sometimes Emma, last night it was Lilly and often, Clara. Greg has even said more often that he is tired of fighting. His body is taking over, he says. He asked me when our plane was leaving tomorrow. Another day he asked me what you pack in your bag when you die.

July 17

Nancy's CaringBridge Letter

The Four E's:

Exhaustion,

Endurance,

Endless Endings.

Catching a few minutes of quiet is rare and I am grateful. Greg is gradually going. It is difficult to accurately portray. He has periods of confusion but can focus sometimes. He is a good actor so if he has a visitor or an overnight person he can pull off the old Greg.

But for those of us here in the trenches, he is pretty much in another world a lot of the time. Sometimes he asks for the walker and wants to get up. It is so painful to hear this request and have to say "no," especially when he told me that he just wanted to go to his own bed and take a hot shower. It is heartbreaking, I feel cruel to explain to him that he can't.

He asked me yesterday what country we were in and told me about a dolphin he saw in the yard. Some people had left that morning on carriages too. I asked him what country he would like us to be in and he said Denmark (not sure where that came from!) Sometimes he will say, "I don't know why I said that," and laugh at himself. He can still be funny and will pop out with something very cogent when we least expect it.

He is eating and drinking small amounts and, unfortunately, eliminating a lot. Half a day can go by for me without anything to account for it but more trash and laundry.

He has less and less interest in going outside and sleeps more at night. Last week he asked me a lot about journeys.

We are talking to him about the experience of letting go and asking him what he needs from us.

Does he want to see anyone or talk to anyone? He seems to feel complete. He has said to me that he just does not know what to "do" about dying. I have faith that he will know the way and I tell him that. He does not need to "do" anymore. He just needs to be…and be loved by all of us.

We no longer talk about things we want to experience together or his goals. We need to help him on his journey and not hinder him with things to stay for. It is difficult to find the way. Of course, we do not want him to go and yet we are so exhausted and wonder how many goodbyes there can be.

How they can continue to be infused with meaning when they are seemingly endless?

We gather around his bed every evening and eat together. Many evenings we have music which we all enjoy. There is a small space beside him in the bed for one of us to snuggle up with him and we love that.

How long a person can live in such an altered reality and maintain sanity? Many days, I think I can't face another and then in equal measure on another day, I feel a power carrying me. I feel envious of those who get to lead a normal life and look forward to being able to make choices for myself about how I spend my time.

I face a bigger unknown world than I can imagine now and I am humbled.

I am grateful for my walks, even when I have to work to put one foot in front of the other. I am grateful for a shower, a cooked meal, a vacuumed house. I feel so frustrated when I see the endless weeds in the garden or the unfinished quilt by my sewing machine. Life is so complicated and so simple at the same time.

Unending love, support and wisdom carry us still.

In gratitude, perplexity and awe.

July 18

NANCY'S CARINGBRIDGE LETTER

Last night I was writing something to be shared with the annual Quaker Gathering of Friends and I want to share this flash of insight this morning.

Several years ago at this same Quaker gathering I listened to someone reflect on an experience: she was called on a path that seemed way beyond her capacity (for her, it was writing a book). She spoke of all that she went through to follow that path even while she questioned her ability to do so. I remember being mystified and wondering if I would ever be called so strongly to follow a path.

I realized today that this is exactly what has been presented to me and what I am doing. This is a sacred journey, we clearly did not choose it and we are learning every step of the way to follow it. Sacred journeys do not always *feel* sacred and we do not always think we know the way.

July 31

NANCY'S CARINGBRIDGE LETTER

Greg is out on the deck where he spent the night. The moon was big and it was cool and dry. The Hospice nurse came today and Greg told him that he is ready to go. He said that this illness has dragged on long enough.

We have not heard him say that exact thing before. He is not talking much and when he does it is often about things that don't make too much sense to us.

He knows we are here and he can ask for what he needs. I think it is a comfort to him to know that we will be ok after he is gone and that we are well taken care of. Yesterday he watched a bit of the Olympics but really wanted men's basketball or the World Series so it was confusing to him that he could not watch either of those.

He is only awake for brief periods of time. He reaches out for my hand and squeezes it and kisses it. He is peaceful and not in pain. He still asks that we get him up and either go upstairs or out to breakfast.

Now I can't fight the tide but I am so angry that this ever had to happen. I really hate this disease and the way it steals away beautiful lives.

We are blessed to have had him as friend, husband, and father. The birds are singing. It is still a beautiful morning.

CHAPTER 25

AUGUST 2012

. . . The secret of life
Is love, which casts its wing
Over all suffering . . .

—Gregory Orr

August 2

NANCY'S CARINGBRIDGE LETTER

Greg had a bit of a resurgence after a rough night a few days ago when he was in a lot of anguish and confused, followed by a day of sleep yesterday.

He was talkative today, ate some blueberries and custard, drank some liquids and was peaceful, happy and funny. We were all four sitting around him this morning and I was feeding him blueberries alternately with droppers of his medication and he said with a big smile, "I don't know what I did to deserve this." He sees things that we don't see and has some pretty odd things to say but none of it bothers him so we all just join in with him and have fun. He is peaceful tonight.

Yesterday was a teary day for all of us. Today we are rolling with it and having a nice evening. Who knows what tomorrow will bring?

August 3

NANCY'S JOURNAL

I know people want to help and care so much but I sometimes just wish people would let me just *BE*. That is what is most helpful… Not helpful to ask me how I am, what they can do to help or in general bother me with questions I can't answer or ones I must to answer to satisfy their curiosity.

August 4

NANCY'S JOURNAL

I hate everything about my abnormal life today. I hate it that I can't be the person I want to be. I can't reciprocate friendships. I am way too oversensitive. I hate it when my children see me cry because they worry. Everyone wants to know how I am. I feel exposed and inadequate. People are in my house all the time.

Everyone wants a piece of Greg or a part in his death while I have already lost him.

I rarely have time alone with the two of us. I can't even remember what it was like when it was just the two of us laughing, problem solving, exploring, gossiping – it is all gone and never will be again.

Others just lose the part of him they know and that is real for them but I have lost so much more because we had our whole lives together.

August 6

NANCY'S JOURNAL

Greg is still asleep and I am holding his hand. It is peaceful. I am thinking about how transformed our lives are now. We are all so fragile. We are always on edge. We can be going along just fine and the slightest comment can set me off and I am infuriated. I can't remember what it was like to not live like this – always on edge.

I look at Greg and I really can't remember – what was he like? I want to remember. I love how funny he is now, though – his sweet smile when he knows he said something goofy. This time of waiting is so unreal. I wonder what it is doing to my insides.

August 9th

NANCY'S CARINGBRIDGE LETTER

A few years ago, our dear friends Elf and Eric presented Greg with a framed drawing of a clump of blueberries. Below it, in calligraphy, is lettered the following explanation of this unusually special species of blueberry:

> *Vaccinium gregareii*
> *A Blueberry of the north country, ranging from Michigan east to Maine and west as far as Alaska. A vigorous upright grower with branches in many directions. Irrepressible by nature, it may benefit from an occasional judicious pruning. Leafs out with optimism even in inclement weather. Its excellent fruit has a*

spirited lively flavor that is naturally engaging to all. Loved by children and shown to be beneficial to their development. Botanists are unclear whether this is a cultivated variety gone wild or a wild strain which has been recently civilized. In either case, this fine berry enjoys an enthusiastic following, especially among the island residents of Puget Sound.

Greg is sleeping most of the day and night. He has about two to three hours of "awake" time and during this time he is often confused about where he is or what is going on. He responds when we orient him to time and place and he is comforted when we remind him that he is on our island in the beautiful house that he built.

He says some very sweet and funny things. He talks a lot about traveling or getting ready for something. He talks about us all going, but "if we get separated..." When he is sleeping he continues to talk, but it is unintelligible. I wonder if he is seeing people from the other side.

He continues to tell us that he is ready to go and when I ask him if he is afraid, he says no. A few times he talked about something really exciting happening but when pressed he can't come up with what it is. I asked him once if the exciting thing happening was about dying and he said: "Now *that* would be a cruel joke!"

He is happy to see us, and smiles when we greet him. He can't initiate conversation but when I ask him if he is sad or scared he says no. I ask if he is comfortable and if he feels safe and loved he always says yes. He has enjoyed some singing around him and some peaceful guitar music.

He is eating minuscule amounts but today ate a blueberry pancake and loved it. Yesterday he woke up for a minute and wanted pizza or a hamburger and told me there were two new places to get them "down that road on the left." Then he fell back asleep. That is how our days go. It is peaceful here in suspended reality, but we are also ready to go on with our lives.

Both worlds live side by side in a way that surprises me. I will fight like hell for one more day when he takes his last breath but I am also ready to be me again and figure out all that it will mean.

It is an odd juxtaposition to remember the family vacations we used to go on at this time of year, and realize that other families still get to go. I feel so sad that our wonderful days as a family of five are over. I know that Greg will always be with us.

There are many goodbyes now, young friends leaving for college or study abroad programs. Most of them have had Greg as a beloved teacher and he is proud of them. Life is bittersweet.

My saddest moments are when I have trouble remembering Greg as he was before this wretched tumor. It all seems so long ago. The last two years have been filled with anguish and grief, although we have also had a lot of fun.

There is a definite line of before and after and sometimes I long for just a moment of remembering what I felt like before. I saw my friend and neighbor yesterday and she told me that there will be many people to "hold the memories." I hope and pray that I will regain them.

August 10

NANCY'S JOURNAL

Greg's last breath at 11:55 pm

August 11

NANCY'S CARINGBRIDGE LETTER

Greg took his last breath last night a few minutes before midnight. We knew he was getting closer yesterday morning and although he was not conscious all day, he was peaceful and we were all five together all day and evening.

We had a beautiful cedar blessing ceremony in the evening outside and we sang to him. We moved him into the living room later in the evening and set up a slumber party all around him. We went to sleep about eleven to the sound of his loud gurgling and the dog snoring. Less than an hour later, Emma heard his last breath and woke us up. He died surrounded by the four women who loved him most. It was just as he wanted it.

Today we have spent the day with beautiful music, candles, friends and fragrant flowers. He is peaceful and the Griz spirit fills the room.

Last night as I tried to go back to sleep, I remembered so many difficult moments in the last two years, amid the joys, and *yes*, there were many, many struggles. He bore his burden nobly and now he can float, dream, visit and fill our lives with more love than we even knew.

He will continue to give to us. I know that. We are all enriched by having known and loved such a man.

Our family is even more enriched by the love and generosity of our many friends and loved ones. We deeply thank you for holding us and helping our hearts chart the course through these rough waters.

With love from us all.

"the end"
by Andrew Michael Roberts

it was the end of something,
and so we grew sad
according to how much we'd loved it.
now, nothing
but our great variety of sadnesses
and for some
a seed of instinct suggesting
something else
may eventually begin.

August 12

NANCY'S CARINGBRIDGE LETTER

Tonight we drove to the school to see this beautiful tribute on the reader board outside:

Goodbye, Old Friend

Be at Peace

August 14

NANCY'S JOURNAL

I feel like I floated over the last two days. But I was here 100%.

Day One – Greg laid out under his Grizzly button blanket for everyone to come and pay their respects. It was beautiful and real – tears, sadness, silliness, wonder, honor, love, respect, relief, grief – all there all day.

Lots of people came through and some stayed to talk, some to cry. It was all as it should be. At 6 p.m. his good friends came back and with the family, we stood around and toasted him. I read poems, we talked about Greg: the hard two years, the love, his friends and his devotion to his family. Then I went outside to the fire, and the man from the funeral home came in and took his body out. I spent the night out by the fire with young people coming in and out. I have spent lots of time out walking. I don't really feel sad yet but I feel such an emptiness, as though something huge has been extracted.

August 15

NANCY'S JOURNAL

Feels so good not to have to get up and worry about Greg. I do not miss his being sick, his ravaged body, his confusion. I don't long for that part. I am sad and angry about the whole thing – the whole two long years, the fact that it ever happened – the sadness of all that we had to go through – all the trauma is what I feel now.

I am comforted by the memories of us together earlier in his illness, when we could grieve together, fight for his life together. But I am not comforted by memories of the last part when he was gone from me. It had to end. His dying had to happen. He died a little bit the moment he was diagnosed. There were so many small deaths along the way. I realize that I never once felt hopeful that he would "beat" the tumor. Maybe I should have? I knew this day would come.

August 16

NANCY'S CARINGBRIDGE LETTER

No one mentioned grocery shopping: it feels strange and sad — no more coffee, peanut butter, frosted flakes or chocolate milk. I got to the store and thought, "really, there just isn't much that I need," after so many years of shopping for our family. It feels more abrupt than I expected even with all of my time to "prepare."

I am more grateful than I can say for all the work we were able to do together before Greg died. He wanted to ease my path. He did so in many ways, and yet, it is just hard.

The girls and I went to the funeral home and now I have the mysterious experience of holding his ashes, less than a week after he died. How is it that a body that carried Greg so many miles, through so many adventures, can be reduced to a large box in a blue velvet bag?

I ask myself often, "Where is he now?" He still feels close but he has not been gone long. No matter what we believe, we don't really know. I know he lives on in all of us, but is his spirit still close by? We all say that he is in a better place, but how do we really know?

I voraciously read near-death experiences to Greg before he died and they were all about a calm, all-knowing, loving place. But none of us really knows what happens, because these stories were from people who came back.

Greg told me many times that he would miss me and even left a letter for me saying the same at the end. I always laughed at him and told him *he* would not have to miss *me*, but we would all have to live missing *him*. Now I think, how do I know that? Maybe he is missing us. These theoretical questions take on so much more meaning to me now. I thought I had firm beliefs about life and death but now I question them all.

What I do know is that his body started failing him two years ago. Although he rarely had much physical pain, he had to endure *a lot* of suffering. He does not have to live with that any more. I don't want him gone but I don't want to live as we were, losing him bit by bit and dreading what was to come. It was a lose/lose game and now that part is over. There is relief in black and white.

My first days of widowhood have been mixed. I needed to get off the island and I have done that. I went to our friend's house where we stayed when Greg had his treatment. I thought it would be difficult but it was oddly comforting. One aspect that C.S. Lewis points out in his book, *A Grief Observed*, is that the loved one is gone no matter where you are and that absence is as palpable in "neutral" territory as it is in more familiar territory. It is just *there*, like a missing body part.

One thing I notice is that I want time to slow down because the more time that goes by, the longer I have been without Greg. I do not want to face life without him.

Now, I must write an obituary. I did not think it would be so hard. I wrote it all in my head but now that I try to get it into words, they are stuck somewhere. It feels important and yet, again, like a box of ashes, how does one distill such a life into a few paragraphs?

Greg was a great man, devoted to what he loved in life. A better husband and father than many. Greg was a mentor and teacher extraordinaire, a loving son and brother and he was human. He had his faults and weaknesses just like all of us. There will never be another Greg.

August 16

NANCY'S CARINGBRIDGE LETTER

I feel deep gratitude to all of you who have loved and held our family: for your encouraging and loving affirmation of our path which now has become my path, for the beautiful flowers adorning my home, for the food that has come our way and continues, for the 4:00 chore guys, for the night guys, for the host of cards that I just sat and read and for the many more personal expressions of love and care that have been bestowed on us. I hope one day to thank each person individually but it will be a while, so in the meantime, please know that even if I have not said a personal thank you that your kindness and gifts of love to us, each is etched on my heart and held there. Not one has gone unnoticed.

August 18

NANCY'S JOURNAL

It's my 62nd birthday. The girls are all here and loving me. Emma made a beautiful cake in the shape of a teapot. They do make a sad birthday happy. I wonder if Greg can know how we are? It is not so much that I want to hear from him yet, as much as I want him to know how we love each other and how we remember him every minute of the day. How my wedding ring on my finger means more than ever. That I went to the art gallery and bought myself a present with his gift certificate, how I talked to

Lilly and I know she will be ok, she is wise. I want him here to talk Clara through the details of her upcoming hiking trip and I want to tell him how the cat threw up on the bedroom carpet and I had to clean it up on my birthday morning. I want to tell him how, in spite of being ok and although I know it has to be this way, in spite of being strong, in spite of everything I miss him. He is such a part of me.

August 19

NANCY'S JOURNAL

The girls need me so much and I need so much to be alone to think and process and figure out what in the hell just happened in my life.

I have adults to lean on. Although the girls have good friends who love them, their friends are young and can't really be depended on. There is only me for them. I miss just touching Greg, his warmth and hearing his breathing. I am forcing myself to walk and water the plants but I see how I could sit in one place and not move, or just go back to bed. And I need to write that damned obituary. Why is that so hard?

August 21

NANCY'S JOURNAL

Yesterday I spent the day making all sorts of "death calls." Calling the life insurance, bank, mortgage, car insurance companies and on and on. It wasn't all that bad. I could do it! But really, I just want to disappear somewhere quiet and have no responsibility. Instead I am cleaning out the house, being here for the girls and hosting Greg's brother who is visiting.

I wonder where Greg is? Today I used his toothpaste and the smell made me sad. I miss him. I can't really miss the before time yet because it was so long ago. How can I miss something that has not existed for two years?

And now there is so much to *do* and there is way too much to comprehend and take in. How is that with grieving? It is a time when action is really hard and yet I need to think!

I need to find photos, write an obituary, keep the flowers watered so they won't die and my brain does not want to work.

It is easier for me to say that Greg has "gone." I can't quite say he is "dead."

August 23

NANCY'S JOURNAL

I am so unproductive. I love all of the cards I get – every day I get more. I will miss them when they stop. Each one connects me to something, either a person or a memory.

I marvel at how people I talk to seem to have such a need for me to "feel better" or have a "better day" than the day before. Why should it matter to anyone but me? Maybe it is good for me to feel bad! Why wouldn't I? My husband of 23 years just died!

What would it say about our whole marriage if I didn't feel bad? And what does "doing ok" even mean? Truthfully, I am walking around with a gigantic hole in the middle of my chest,

I am in shock and I will never have Greg again...never have someone at my side when my girls get married or someone to share grandchildren with. It is all over, so how could I possibly be ok?

On some level, there is a big part of me that does not really believe Greg is gone and that scares me a bit. I am afraid that all of a sudden it will hit me and I will crumble to the floor.

August 25

NANCY'S CARINGBRIDGE LETTER

Everything that is said about grieving rings true: the waves, the feeling of walking through mud, the hole/amputation feeling, the lack of productivity, the deep sadness and yes, also a relief in a way. As I sort through many details, I miss Greg more than I ever thought possible. I don't think it has sunk in that he is not coming back.

The memorial service will be on our island and we are madly working on details and location. We have had many discussions and we feel clear that an outside venue is necessary for the Greg spirit. We often called him "Mr. Blue Sky." I hope he can provide on that day or you will need your umbrellas!!

It will be held at 2:00 pm on September 16th, location to be announced. It corresponds with the ferry schedule for those coming from for the day from off island locations.

August 25

NANCY'S JOURNAL

My sweet, beloved Phoebe dog has a malignant tumor. It has been removed but why do I have *this?* I feel totally immobilized – radiation, dog oncologist. I wanted a break from these words and somehow I thought I might be "deserving" of that break? Ridiculous! Of course I am not. So now I feel like I have been thrown back into a swimming whirlpool that I can't get out of.

August 26

NANCY'S JOURNAL

I feel a physical pain in my chest. I really hurt so much more than I ever thought possible. I know that it will get better because everyone says it will get better but it does not feel like it will. I can't make any decisions. I have to make decisions about the memorial and I just want others to decide for me....even what to eat and when I should go for a walk. I feel so overwhelmed and I question my "mental competence to stand trial." I just can't fathom having the energy to *live* again. I will just exist and I won't know how to really *live* without Greg.

August 27

NANCY'S JOURNAL

Feeling lighter today. That works for me to say rather than "better." Today is our anniversary. Greg is closer today. Does he know it is our anniversary? Does he like the obituary I wrote?

August 27

NANCY'S CARINGBRIDGE LETTER

I wrote Greg's obituary. I felt so much responsibility to represent Greg in the way he would want. I never imagined how difficult it would be. I submitted it today.

I am away from home for a couple of days and it feels good. I wish I could say that home is my place of solace but that is not true yet. I hope it will change. Sometimes my heart feels lightened up and sometimes grief feels like physical pain.

Without diminishing my experience, I am aware of many others I know who have had similar or worse losses. I know that they have integrated the loss, which helps me know that I will as well.

The girls similarly move in and out of their strong emotions. I like to think we help each other and I suppose we do, yet we each must find our way.

I love the flowers that so many have sent to me. What a tradition it is, to send flowers to a bereaved family: now I understand it. They bring great joy with their color, fragrance and life. I have received many cards and they are each unique.

I take time each day to sit with each card and think of the sender with gratitude.

OBITUARY

Gregory Albert Ewert, beloved husband, father, friend, teacher extraordinaire, mentor, uncle, brother, photographer, juggler, outdoor adventurer, pilot, sailor, mountain climber, table tennis player and devoted community member died peacefully in his home on our island, Washington, minutes before midnight on August 10, 2012. He was surrounded by the four people he loved most in the world: his wife, Nancy, and daughters, Emma, Lilly and Clara.

Greg's life began February 11, 1949 in Lansing, Michigan, where he grew up in a lively family of seven and learned early to explore the world that always so delighted him. In 1967, he left home to attend school at the University of Washington, beginning a never-ending love affair with the Pacific Northwest.

Greg majored in architecture at the UW and was able to work with photographers he admired. Eventually, he ended up with a teaching degree that navigated him to a passion that became his life's work, always incorporating his skills in photography. Greg's long teaching career began in 1977 in Seattle at The Little School, continued in Ambler AK, and back to Seattle at Lakeside School.

He was a founder of Coyote Central, a successful community-based learning program connecting middle school students with creative professionals, and he continued to be a passionate supporter of its work and values.

While in college, Greg took a kayak trip to the San Juan Islands and, ten years later, fulfilled his dream to purchase land on our island. He met Nancy in 1987 and, a year later, they married and moved full time to our island. Greg designed the home he and Nancy built together and raised their three children while Greg worked full time teaching, first on neighboring Shaw Island in a one-room schoolhouse. After two years there, he started teaching at the our island School. Over his years there, Greg taught fifth grade, developed and taught in the Alternative K-5 program in the our island Elementary School, and finally, our island Middle School. While he taught all subjects, he was especially appreciated for his ability to help all students succeed in math. In 2002, Greg and family went on a Fulbright teaching exchange to Exeter, England, where he taught at Stoke Canon School for a year, one full of delightful memories and lifelong friendships.

As a teacher, Greg believed most important learning takes place outside of the four walls of the classroom and encouraged his students to discover and explore their interests. He saw the uniqueness in each student, and he led them to believe in themselves and to know that they could do whatever they wanted. A mentor and friend to many students without healthy adult role models, he was a passionate supporter of experiential education and exemplified its success.

A family man, Greg was fortunate to have been able to teach each of his daughters in the classroom. As a family, they had numerous adventures and Greg, with his "can do" attitude, was always ready for another. He led his daughters to delight in the outdoors through mountain hikes, boating and camping trips, remaining undaunted in his love for yet another fun family adventure.

Greg was a dreamer and a visionary. He fulfilled many of his dreams but always had more. He had a passion for life that many would say was unequaled. His passion took him all over the US and Canada in his youth and, in adulthood, from Alaska to Russia, Japan, England, and Europe as well as on multiple school outdoor trips and school service-learning trips to Nicaragua. He photographed and co-published an award-winning book, *Kindred Spirits*, in 2001. He was most happy sleeping under the stars and only used a tent if he absolutely had to. He fulfilled his life-long dream of becoming a pilot in 2006 and loved every minute in the air.

Diagnosed in August 2010 with a glioblastoma brain tumor, Greg lived with his illness the same way he lived his life: with zest. He maintained his sense of humor, courage and optimism until the day he died. He deeply understood what real learning meant and continued to share this passion throughout his illness. He was noble and graceful as his body failed him. The world is a better place with Greg's mark on it.

Greg is survived by his wife, Nancy; daughters Emma, Lilly and Clara; brother, David Ewert; sisters, Jane Ewert, Mary VanWylen and Cathy Benson; and nieces and nephews, Jessica, Sarah, Erika, Nick, Lauren, Jack and Christopher.

CHAPTER 26

SEPTEMBER 2012

Though we need to weep your loss,
You dwell in that safe place in our hearts,
Where no storm or night or pain can reach you.

—John O'Donohue,
"On the Death of the Beloved"

September 1

NANCY'S CARINGBRIDGE LETTER

Ahhhhh, grief: it is vivid and real. It feels like a genuine physical ache somewhere in my body. Today I thought, "I have a gouge the size of the Grand Canyon down the middle of my body." It is palpable and it comes barging in with the power of a tsunami. Even the full moon felt heartbreaking to me, remembering all those full moons with Greg.

Grief, at times, has complete control of my mind without my knowing it. I think I am functioning with some semblance of normalcy but then I completely forget what I just talked to someone about. It feels like my psyche is being controlled by an outside force and it is embarrassing and disconcerting.

I am trying to plan this big memorial for Greg and have a lot of other details to hold together but it is hard to trust myself completely.

I spent the weekend cleaning, which feels good until I kept running into Greg's belongings. I opened one of his dresser drawers and immediately felt searing pain. I am gathering photos and sometimes I can look at them nostalgically and smile, other times it's a punch in the gut. I still don't really understand he is gone for good.

I notice too, how we human beings always want each other to "feel better" or be "doing ok." It fascinates me because I have no need to feel "better" or to feel anything other than what I feel.

If my heart feels lighter for a while, so be it, but if I am hurting, well, why wouldn't I? How could someone want me not to? I have just endured two years watching the love of my life and father of my children gradually be robbed of life and now I have to face the rest of my life without him. How or why should I "feel better" or be "doing OK"? If I did, I would not be doing Greg or our long marriage justice. Words fail us. We humans are complex and resilient.

Planning for the memorial is well underway with many hands making lighter work. I continue to be completely amazed at the generosity of this community and am touched deeply every day by the power of love in action.

Greg's brain surgery was two years and two weeks ago yesterday. It feels like a lifetime ago and I guess it was. We are all changed. We all hurt and we all miss Greg and always will. I still wonder where he is? I wonder this a lot. I miss him more than I ever thought possible.

September 2

NANCY'S JOURNAL

It is *very* strange to be alone, to come home to a dark house – no Greg, sick or well, anywhere in this world. Today I was cleaning up my sewing stuff and here was his purple t-shirt with the back cut open so we could get it on him when he was bedridden. It was on his body with his skin touching it and I held it close to me but there is no body left to be on the other side of that fabric. How can it be?

It is shocking to me that this has happened. I am being carried in a boat down a river but I did not choose to get into that boat and I don't have a lot of input about where it is going now. It is just going.

September 4

NANCY'S JOURNAL

I hurt more than ever. Not less, more. I know that what I went through in the last four months was hell and I wanted it to be over. But now what? I can't say I want all of that back but I can't honestly say I don't. So far this new territory is no easier. I still miss Greg in an acutely painful way. I am amazed at how I long to touch his warm body with blood coursing through it, even when he couldn't offer anything back. How I long to feel him squeeze my hand. I am trying to think of things that irritated me about him so I don't have to long for him so much. I need to make phone calls and do something besides sitting here crying. Sometimes I think I can't do this. I wish I knew when we would be together again or *if* we will when I die. There are just no words for this pain.

September 6

NANCY'S CARINGBRIDGE LETTER

Join us to Remember a Beautiful Life
Sunday September 16th, 2pm-5pm
Hoedemaker's Farm
2036 Davis Bay Road, our island

The Memorial will be outdoors

Dress for the weather, Remember Greg,
Mr. Blue Sky, was never deterred by weather.

Please wear appropriate shoes
for a walk from the parking area across
the field to a stunning memorial site.

Arrangements are made for those for whom walking is more difficult.

Straw bale seating, bring a blanket for seat comfort and/or warmth.

September 8

NANCY'S JOURNAL

I actually had an OK day with a good walk with a friend. Calm afternoon but then tonight, I feel so sad. It is so heavy, this sadness. I am afraid it will not get any better.

September 10

NANCY'S JOURNAL

How can it have been a month? What doesn't make me sad? It feels like Greg's living and all of that caring and work was so long ago and yet I can't believe it has been an entire month.

Does he fade away as time goes on? I looked so forward to going on with my life…to having a life but every step in that direction is a step away from my life with Greg. I don't want to leave him. I don't want to say "single" on my W-2 form. I don't want the new checks I had to get with only my name on them.

I am excited about going to California to look at schools with Clara. It is such a mixed bag. Last night I was with good friends and while I loved being with them, it makes the loss so *evident*. He is *so* not there, where he should be. I feel stupid wondering if he can see us. I wish I had some kind of communication with him. I completely understand why people try to contact the dead. I think it would help me move on if I knew something about him.

I never would have predicted this part – my obsession with where he is. I think the idea of dying will never be scary for me if it means the chance of seeing Greg again.

September 14

NANCY'S JOURNAL

Now I have to face this weekend with the memorial and then it will be all over. Scary! I don't want it to go too fast. Everyone who comes for the memorial shares their shock and grief that Greg is not here, and it is so hard to be gracious amidst all of my own suffering, fear, and exhaustion. I am quite sure I am not doing it well.

The memorial planning is such a production. I worry that we can get lost in producing the event and lose Greg in it. Then I look at his photo and I think, "Wow, are you really gone? Is this why you were here? Where are you and how did this happen to us? How did you get sick?"

I can easily focus on the sweet times, the more intimate times, the times when just our family mattered.

September 16

NANCY'S JOURNAL

Greg's memorial is today. There was a big party last night with lots of people. Too many people, too much drinking. I hope it was fun for everyone else. I regretted doing it about the moment it started.

Now it is morning and I want to feel a connection with Greg – I just knew in a minute what I wanted to do – I took his ashes to his special spot. I touched them for the first time. Fragments of Greg in my fingers, and buried them right where he put his first building on our land. So today we say goodbye to him. I can't even imagine how, and yet all along for two years, I knew this moment would come. I imagined it often so it seems part of the natural progression. But underneath there is chaos, insanity, unbelievable.

How can this be? Where are you? I wish he could be buried here so I could lay down on top of him.

September 21

NANCY'S CARINGBRIDGE LETTER

I want to share words about the Memorial on Sunday but I don't have them yet. Suffice it to say that it was one of the most incredible days in my life. We made a sacred space and Greg was honored as he should have been. We talked, sat, sang and cried with love that we all experienced deep into our bones. It was holy and it stays with me today.

I do not have the words, but the poet Jessica Gigot wrote this about the day:

from "Making Ceremony by the Sea"

Pacific

Sitting on hay bales
We look out at the Sound,
The Olympics and
Exsiccated pasture.
A Haida button blanket
Is draped over cedar logs
Laid between a vibraphone
And a stone-rimmed fire pit.
His wife, an old student
And a men's club friend
Speak their respects
Before we all stand
To send his bear spirit
Beyond a new moon sunset.

—Jessica Gigot

September 26

NANCY'S JOURNAL

It's hard to help Clara with everything related to her senior year and college search. I am just not that strong right now. I do so wish for some all-knowing force to come in and take over. I don't want to feel so responsible. I want to be taken care of. I feel helpless and inept.

September 28

NANCY'S JOURNAL

It feels like Greg is gone now... more gone. The fact that he is not here – that *huge* heavy weight is always with me whether I am asleep or awake. It neither feels bad or good, it just *is*. It is infused with the love and world I had with Greg.

I am different from who I was before I knew him. I can manage alone. I have the experience and competence to live alone but Greg is a part of me now. I am not just me in the world, I am me and all of our 24 years together. I am just beginning to understand how he remains a part of me. It is more than just memories. It is incorporated into all that I am.

I feel lighter today and more energetic. Not as though heavy boots are walking across my heart but more like sandals.

September 30

NANCY'S CARINGBRIDGE LETTER

I look at this blank page and I think: "Where *do* I start?" And then I realize that this is the phrase that sums up my life right now.

It is a long road and feels difficult and sad. That is not to say I can't function normally and have normal conversations, because I can and do.

The good parts are that I can focus on other people and their lives and not have this huge uncertainty in the background all the time lurking and distracting me.

I can start to do things for others. I cooked a meal for another family this week, which felt big. I have finally finished straightening out most of the details that one must do when someone dies: the lawyer, the endless phone calls to change names of accounts and documents, notifying institutions of his death. I went to our local bank and as soon as I sat down to begin to say what I needed, I cried and could not stop. With care, they brought me a box of tissues and gently said, "This happens here sometimes."

Underlying it all is this huge deep chasm of longing, disbelief, deep sadness and unknowing. It comes and goes and I know that I need to be with it all, walk with it, delve into it, cry about it and continue living this beautiful life. It is a puzzle beyond all puzzles.

The aspect that I hate the most is that I don't have Greg here to talk about it with. It is hard beyond the definition of hard. It is often described but can't be conveyed. I am surprised at how much I can miss him.

During our lives together, we had a good flow of being independent of each other and it was fun to do things apart. I lived for many of my adult years completely independently before I met him, so I honestly thought this would be somehow "easier" for me, which I am embarrassed to admit. Even when he was so sick and confused he was still here in a way that he is not now. The big empty hole is enormous and echoing.

We had a good life together and missing him does not negate a day of it. No one can take away the love and happiness that we shared and the memories are rich and full but it still comes down to living without him.

How on earth will l manage a house and five acres on my own? There is so much that he tracked and knew needed to be done and it feels overwhelming to me. I will muddle through, I know I will, but how?

I went to a Grief group this week on the mainland. There was one woman there whose husband died just after Greg and she really spoke my mind. It was amazing to hear her say almost everything I have felt and said, even if just to myself. The downside is that the group is on the mainland and takes a full day of ferries to get there and home.

I have a couple of books that I find helpful also and there is comfort in knowing that everything I am feeling is so normal. I have utter confidence that I will find my way and I look at others who have been down this road and marvel at how easy they made it look.

The irony is that there is so little that others can do to ease the way but without all of you wonderful, solid friends I know I could never make it through another hour. Again, I marvel at the power of bearing witness to each other's life experience: how just by knowing, listening, walking alongside each other through our joy and pain, even at a distance, we hold each other up. It will never cease to be less than miraculous for me to know this simple fact.

When I try to write about Greg's memorial, I can't do it justice. It was the most beautiful, full and sacred day of my life. There was clearly a power there beyond we mortals, and I am eternally grateful. So much work by a multitude of human hands made it all happen and the gift is etched on the hearts of all who attended, not the least of which is mine.

It was an experience of the transcendent power of love that we don't normally access in our daily lives. A life well-lived and known leaves us with many lessons.

The girls are all back into their lives. Emma is beginning the life of a college graduate – working, paying student loans and thinking about what comes next. She lives in her little cabin that Greg worked so hard to remodel for her and she is happy to be here for now.

Lilly is back in school in Oregon which is overwhelming after the first week but she loves living in her own house and has a great support system.

Clara is full on with her senior year and college applications. Last summer she started horseback riding again and it is her greatest joy right now. She is doing her senior project on Equine Therapy.

Greg would be so proud of them all and that feels comforting to me.

I cherish words of encouragement, each card, the flowers, the prayers, all that friends have done and do. I know Greg leaves a hole in many lives and that the learning will be lifelong.

CHAPTER 27

OCTOBER/NOVEMBER/ DECEMBER 2012

Relief, release. And love
That goes past death, that
Keeps the connection
So many think death severs.

—Gregory Orr

October 3

NANCY'S JOURNAL

I had some moments yesterday when I realized I was not think-ing about Greg. It was a busy day, the hot tub was leaking, the smoke alarm was beeping and I got out the ladder and fixed it. I was proud of myself. It was way up high and I did it.

October 7

NANCY'S JOURNAL

I woke up in the night last night and felt so sad. How strange to feel sad in my sleep. I had a pretty good day yesterday. I went for a walk with B (also a widow) and talked and cried a bit. She told me more about her experience and definitely normalized everything I said, which helped. I did not have the feeling that I need to be doing better as I have with some people.

October 21

NANCY'S JOURNAL

For the first time, I feel like I have moved into a new phase. I went out Friday night to a fundraising event and enjoyed it. I am taking in more of the outside world. I am no longer the center of attention everywhere I go and it feels good. I am beginning my new life. I called the school about getting on the substitute list. It has been exactly five days since my last day of crying all day. I am not calling it a major shift but it feels good. I think how happy Greg would be, knowing that we are doing just what we need to do. I am not identifying my days by his death anymore.

October 31

NANCY'S JOURNAL

I am moving along, taking care of so many details of life. I feel empowered by it. But then it worries me that I have not felt as sad lately. I am afraid it will come back to haunt me. But can't I just feel good while I do and face the rest when it comes? It is just a mystery to me why this isn't harder now.

November 20, 2012

NANCY'S JOURNAL

... "You'll get over it" they say
And maybe, after years you do,
Or at least some of the time when
It's quiet, or during music, you almost do.

—William Stafford, "Tragedy"

So many tears shed lately between the girls and me. It takes a lot of time to be sad. I look at our wedding photo now – Greg – where is he? What in the heck happened here? I still don't quite get it. It feels like he must be somewhere else not far away. I know he is not here – I do know he is not coming back but he must be somewhere, because how can he just be gone?

I try to remember Greg when he was healthy and quite honestly, I can't conjure up that memory. I remember events, but not him. I can kind of hear his voice and I remember his boundless energy, but what was our life really like?

I vividly remember everything after his diagnosis. I remember how he felt and how I felt and then I feel so very sad for us. So sad for him to have to wither away. He clung so hard to life. I often remember the trauma and all of the unending feeling that this would go on forever, while feeling like I could not take another day.

He made life so complicated for all of us when he couldn't give up anything and he pushed and pushed. Was it just simply bad judgement because of the tumor or was it his personality of always "making things happen"? I feel guilty that it was so hard for me and that I could not embrace all he wanted with more enthusiasm.

Now it is almost Thanksgiving, then Christmas. I know the tradition is so important to the girls. I would like to blink and have it all over. I can't figure out what any of it all means anymore. I used to think it meant something to me but now I don't know what anything means.

December 5

NANCY'S CARING BRIDGE LETTER

What if we never 'get over' certain deaths . . .
What if the idea that we should have by now, or
will, is a great palace lie?

—Anne Lamott

Can it really be December?

It is amazing how life goes on. The sun rises and sets every day. The moon waxes and wanes, the seasons change. There is dinner to be cooked every night and bills to be paid. The world is full and rich and I have a good life. It is strange to me that I can just go on and feel relatively happy and then all of the sudden I will REMEMBER and I realize how I live in this constant juxtaposition of the beauty of life that I feel so deeply and the loss of Greg.

A lot of my focus is on the girls, especially Clara, who is busy in her senior year of high school and looking toward what is next. I am thankful for this time with her, for the routine of our days, for the ways in which she needs me and how it keeps me in the present. It is a good focus and I am ever aware of the bittersweet changes in my role of parenting. In less than a year, I will be alone after 23 years of taking care of my children and family.

Now it is also the dreaded time for those who have lost a loved one known as "The Holidays." I won't say it is not hard. It is hard. The days are dark and short. It is cold and rainy every day. My life and our home is filled with memories and I miss Greg more than I can say. Sometimes I have to check the box "widowed" or tell someone to take his name off of an account. I don't want anyone to think it is because we are divorced so then I find myself explaining that he has died. During those moments, the wound is opened and fresh.

I'm still traumatized by the last two years and all that fell on my shoulders. I know that I am recovering from it all and I don't know how long it will take. In many ways, I cannot believe that Greg is really gone. I can hardly make myself say the word "dead." It just feels too bleak and final. I look at his photo and he is alive and eager to be part of this world, so how can he be dead?

But clearly, he *is* gone. He is not here. I am the only parent my children have. I am the only one they come to with their sadness and grief. I feel the weight and responsibility while I am grateful that they rely on me.

Sometimes I wonder if I have even begun my life as a widow. I often feel suspended in some undefined space of time, as though I am between three realities: the one I once knew, the one I was thrust into for two years, and whatever is to come – the future, the great unknown.

Then there is the world that I can't share with Greg anymore. I long to share so much of it with him. I want to tell him how kind people are to me, how when I go into the school, kids come up and hug me. How his favorite mechanic has taken such good care of Clara and me, how the deputy called to tell us that her "Classic Car" license plate really is *not* ok for daily driving even though Greg swore to us it was. How I almost called a plumber because I heard water running and thought there was a leak inside the wall, only to discover that it was the outside faucet which was left on.

We are most fortunate that the experience of Greg's illness has given us a bond that is deep beyond words. We need each other and we depend on each other in a way we never knew before. I realized on Thanksgiving that when we are all four together, there is a way that Greg is with us. He is such an integral part of each of us as individuals and when we are all together, it is magnified times four.

December 25th 2012

Nancy's Caring Bridge Letter

La Manzanilla, Mexico

Today we decided our way to honor Greg would be a Christmas day swim in the ocean while scattering some of his ashes.

As we were walking down the beach looking for a quiet place to execute our plan, I saw a boat on the beach with the name "GREGOR" painted on the side. I am usually a bit of a skeptic when people talk about signs from their loved ones who have passed on, but I will be the first to admit that this gave me pause. Obviously, this was our place.

We miss him. It is difficult to get through one of his favorite seasons without him, but in spite of this, we're having a really good time here.

It was hard and lonely as I knew it would be. I am learning all the time how many layers of emotion we are capable of living with – and they are all real. I can be deeply sad and yearn for Greg while at the same time recognizing beauty and feeling great joy. This concept mystifies me and at the same time I know it is truth.

I sometimes question how much I really accept the finality that Greg's life has ended. It continues to be a complex and confusing experience. I try to embrace it with the faith that I will find my way.

I was marveling this week, remembering the time when all three girls were teenagers and I wondered if I could make it through. It was not easy. Now I know so clearly that they are my life's great blessing. I will never be alone on any holiday if they have anything to do with it. They are devoted, loving and under-standing. I really am fortunate beyond what I ever imagined.

In this way, the year comes to a close. I am relieved to say we made it this far. We have a bond that many families are not blessed with. It is a lot of work, sometimes. But we know we need each other and that the love we shared with Greg carries us, always.

CHAPTER 28

2013

Someday I'll get over you.
I'll live to see it all through.
But I'll always miss,
Dreaming my dreams with you.

—Waylon Jennings, "Dreaming My Dreams
with You"

January 3, 2013

NANCY'S JOURNAL

Oh, where do I begin in my lost list of thoughts and feelings? I am ever so happy that 2013 has come. It really feels like I can turn a corner – dare I say that I HAVE turned a corner? I don't know but I do have some extra psychic space. There is some newly re-created me who wants to be revealed. I know that and can feel it bubbling. My task is to pay attention to that "me" and not let her melt into everyone else. I have loved being a mother and wife for 24 years. Greg and I did a great thing. We had a good marriage and we were good partners and parents. But I know there is so much more for me. I don't resent for a minute the hard parts of partnership and love. But I don't feel for a minute that because he is gone, my life has ended. I am scared of the insecurity of life alone and afraid that I can't be enough for my children - that I will miss something that they need.

January 20

NANCY'S CARING BRIDGE LETTER

You will never be alone, you hear so deep
a sound when autumn comes.
. . . that's what the silence meant: you're not alone.
The whole wide world pours down.

—William Stafford, "Assurance"

Hidden grief: Is this an actual term? I am experiencing it lately. Here is how it feels: The world, my friends, my children and even I, all "go on" with life. None of us can stop living or even slow the flow of life. New people get sick, other tragedies happen, there are joys, accomplishments, the seasons turn, and there are more beautiful sunrises and sunsets. The world has needs that call forth and we answer. I am just as much a part of all of these aspects of life as I ever was – I would even say more a part. I feel each joy and sorrow more deeply now.

But underneath it all is a river of loss that never stops flowing. I'm not in that river all the time but I dip into it when I least expect it. I feel all of the sadness, outrage, and yearning for my life with Greg that I ever felt. But what happens now is that I feel all this *while living my daily life.* So it's as though that part of me becomes invisible to others.

I am no longer as isolated as I was and I want to belong to life and my community, and even I tend to "forget" where I am in this process. I forget how tender I feel, how much care I need. I forget that, I can certainly understand why it seems that others do also.

Just a couple of days ago, I was in a quilt shop. A woman was buying some beautiful bear-themed Northwest Indian art fabric and talking about how she was making a quilt for her husband. It was such Greg fabric. Immediately, tears welled up in my eyes. It took all I had to just do what I was doing and not make a fool out of myself in public. These moments come when I least expect them.

I miss Greg most sometimes for the girls. I feel so sad and angry that they no longer have a Dad. I can accept the fact that I no longer have a husband but it feels unfair that at their ages, they have to live without Greg. It's more than living without a Dad because it is living without Greg, who was Super Dad. They all miss him so much.

I have a tendency to feel unrealistically responsible for trying to not only be a good Mom but also give them something of what Greg would give them. .

I ask myself a lot: "What would Greg say or do in this situation?" It's partly good, because I can still glean his perspective. But it's not good that I often feel less than adequate – not enough for them. I might have some good parenting qualities, but I will never be Greg.

It feels complicated to always want to incorporate him into my life/our lives and also to go on without him. So much of my daily life is still about him. Even if it is just the grief work, it is about losing him – this is the invisible part.

And having said all of this, I move on. I look forward to my future, whatever it holds. I am grateful for the stability in my life and for my steadfast friends who never leave me. I see this as a time to fertilize the ground for what is to come. I have recognized that I am, by nature, an optimistic person and I am grateful for that.

Phoebe, the dog, who had a malignant tumor removed after Greg died and then a course of chemo, seems to be doing very well. She remains our constant companion and bearer of great joy.

Gratitude has become a foundation of my life.

February 1, 2013

NANCY'S JOURNAL

> *If deepest grief is hell,*
> *Then the world returning*
> *(Not soon, not easily)*
> *Must be heaven.*
>
> —Gregory Orr

I feel lost and rudderless. I think about all this time when I have been doing okay and now I feel so *not* okay. Is this the way it is going to be? I had all of this time to catch up with my friends and my life and now that I have caught up, I don't know where to go or what to do from here. It was always so helpful to have Greg to talk to at times of confusion. He could help me make sense of the world and now I have no one.

February 11, 2013

NANCY'S CARING BRIDGE LETTER

If we're not supposed to dance,
Why all this music?

—Gregory Orr

Sixty-four years ago, tomorrow, Greg was born. Six months ago today he died. It seems concise and simple as I see it written and yet those sixty-four years were so full. These six months feel equally empty, sometimes.

The first six months were full of just catching up with myself. There was a relief from the constant adrenaline of two years of watching, protecting, advocating, worrying, managing, anticipating and caregiving. Now, perhaps, relief has run its course, leaving more room for the sadness and the missing.

I am literally surprised at times how many tears a body can produce over and over again. I can mostly hold it together in public but not always. It is comforting to live in such a small, loving community when I can't quite keep the tears at bay.

And yet, I am taking baby steps to create a new life.

We had a birthday party for Greg on Friday with our friends who celebrated with him for many birthdays. He would always say he just wanted to have a few friends over for dinner and before I knew it, he had invited twenty-five people! He always loved it, so last year I promised him we'd keep celebrating him every year. I made his favorite cake and we sang Happy Birthday and blew out the candles. To my surprise, it was fun.

Sometimes I feel like Scarlett O'Hara sighing and saying, "Tomorrow is another day." But that thought holds wisdom, as the unknown continues to unfold.

March 4, 2013

NANCY'S JOURNAL

Be patient, Dear Heart,
I'm learning how
to love you dead.

—Donna Hilbert, "In Quintana Roo"

Feels like time is going by too fast – I am not sure of the too fast – for what? In a way, too fast for me in relation to losing Greg. I don't want him to be just a fading memory in my life. I hate that experience of being out and about and being single. I liked being part of a couple and a family, having that sense of belonging to someone and something. Now I am on my own and feel adrift out here. I feel myself teetering on the edge of a full-fledged identity crisis and it feels so scary. I pull myself back and breathe. I know I am okay.

May 9, 2013

NANCY'S CARINGBRIDGE LETTER

. . . Life itself
Was full of mystery —
Why shouldn't the life
After death be strange?

—Gregory Orr

Sometimes I forget how hard our life was a year ago. I don't remember how I felt every day. When I look back at what I wrote a year ago, I honestly can't imagine how we made it through.

As we go through the first spring without Greg, I miss him more than ever. And oh, how I wish it were easier. For reasons I don't understand, it feels harder to me now than any time previously.

I don't know if trying to understand it makes any sense anyway. It is a big loss and every experience of loss is unique.

Feeling it all is exhausting and I want to just feel better. Sometimes I do and sometimes I can't.

Recreating life is difficult. Every way that I have felt valued for these years is changing and I am in the middle of it all without a clear direction. I do not remember a time in my life, ever, that I could say that I honestly do not know what my dreams are. It is not where I thought I would be or where I chose to be and it is a lot of work to make sense of it all.

Grieving is not for the faint of heart and it is full of surprises. I can feel competent and resilient one day and fall apart the next. I never imagined that I would struggle more now than I did during the first half of the year. I know that there is no healthy way to short circuit the process, but that knowledge does not seem to make it easier.

I have a deep understanding that many of our lives are interspersed with struggles and grief. I never delude myself into thinking that my hurts are any more difficult to bear than another's. Every word I have ever read about grieving rings true to my experience at one time or another and in this way, I understand it is universal to us all.

August 10, 2013

Nancy's CaringBridge Letter

I promise I'll never let go
For love is a song
That once started, plays on . . .
And the music, both of us know

b.j.m., "Afterword"

A year has passed since Greg died. A year is a long time. I re-member almost every detail of this day last year. How strange it was to start a day with Greg alive and end it with him gone.

I have few regrets. I have often thought how much love carried him on his transition out of this world. It is stunning to me how powerful is the force of that love.

As much as we were blessed with the grace and strength to do all that we did for Greg, I find myself resenting that he had to live for so long in a diminished state. I hate that it's such hard work to remember the vital, alive, bright, competent and loving man with whom I lived for all of those years.

It is easy to remember the struggling, demanding, "not all there" Greg that he was for those months before he died. Only now can I really see how much he changed with his tumor. It is difficult to incorporate the experience of watching a loved one's brain and body deterioration when it is happening bit by bit, day by day. I am struck by the cruelty of the loss in the way he had to go. I also see the gifts that all that time of knowing brought to us.

Of course, it is a futile mental exercise to ponder these lifelong questions about death, but I hope that Greg's vital self will win out in the end in my memory. His ability to express his love for me and my girls was never compromised by his brain dysfunction. That is surely something to be grateful for.

I am more appreciative than ever for all the great photos I have of Greg, and grateful to those who took them. It helps bring him back in the way I want to remember him.

I feel triumphant to see where we all are at this year marker. I am not naive enough to think we are beyond our grief, any of us, but when I look at our family now, I recognize the blessings that have been bestowed on us allowed us to blossom as we have.

In a way, loss expands as time goes on like a drop of ink on a paper towel. And I suppose in the same way, the loss is absorbed by all of us and we fit around it as it becomes part of who we are.

For me this year has been as hard as the first year is reported to be. But I also am aware of the payoff of hard work. I socialize more comfortably, and I don't feel as raw.

I miss Greg with a painful stab more times than I would like, but it does not stop me in my tracks the way it did for a while. Paradoxically, sometimes I hate the idea that as time marches on, he feels farther away. While I am relieved of some of the burden of new, fresh grief, I also want to hold on to every moment so that he does not slip farther away.

Lilly had a dream a couple of nights ago: "It was the 10th of August and a bunch of us were swimming in the ocean and some dolphins swam by, then Orca whales then a grizzly bear swam by. An airplane flew overhead and we all knew he was with us."

I guess that says it all.

I am going to take a big trip in October. It was Greg and my wish together that I take some of his ashes and scatter them at Dartmoor National Park in England, close to where we lived for our year in England and a place where Greg spent many a delightful hour.

I remember when he was first diagnosed and I was obsessed with the thought that there are people who die alone. How could this be? And how is it that our family has so much of an abundance of love? That will be one of many mysteries that will fill me with wonder for the remainder of my days.

All I can say I know for sure is that we are meant to walk with each other as we all navigate the deep joys and sorrows which make up the mystery that we call our lives. I feel such gratitude for all who walk with me.

To linger in the longing, the loss, the yearning is a way of feeling the rich and embroidered texture of life, the torn cloth of our world that is endlessly being ripped and rewoven.

—Douglas Abrams, *The Book of Joy*

EPILOGUE

There's a thread you follow. It goes among
things that change. But it doesn't change. . . .

Tragedies happen . . .
and you suffer and get old.
Nothing you do can stop time's unfolding.
You don't ever let go of the thread.

—William Stafford, "The Way It Is"

April 1, 2018

On a recent, chilly Friday night, I watched the movie *Coco* while sitting in my living room in front of the big stone fireplace. As I watched, I was surprised as tears streamed down my cheeks. The theme song, "Remember Me," was my undoing. The general theme of the movie is the longing of the dead to be remembered, the difficulty of saying goodbye, and the concept that the dead are never really gone from us.

I never stop missing Greg, but I forget just how tender that place is in my heart: that place that cries for the grandchildren he will never know, but who will learn to love him through our rich stories. He is still a husband, father, and will be a grandfather one day. Greg cries out to be remembered, and it is our task to try to remember him in his wholeness. As time goes on, our family stories rarely feature Greg as one-dimensional, but rather who he was, warts and all, and not surprisingly, there is no shortage of tales.

For these last six years, this remembering has been an easier task than I imagine it might be in ten or twenty. I live in the world Greg imagined and dreamed of, and one that we created together. The strong, peeled trunks of the Doug fir that hold huge beams above me were hewn by Greg's hand at the co-owned saw mill he started. Everywhere I gaze, there are reminders of our life together: tiles given as a wedding gift embedded in the stonework of the hearth; a photo of the English countryside he took on a shared morning walk fifteen years ago; gifts he gave me for various occasions adorn our home, such as the rock with the word "laugh" engraved in it.

What to make of this time out of time since he has left this earthly plane? There is so much to say that it is hard to distill. Loss is much more complicated than I ever knew or could imagine. I venture to guess that the deep loss of a beloved is more complex than any of us know until we walk tentatively down that path. I think, at first, I imagined that I would somehow recover, as one does from pneumonia. I did not imagine it would be easy, but I know myself to have a strong core that I knew would hold.

Ahh, there is so much I did not know, and I am aware that there will be much to learn as I live in this world of someone who has experienced a great loss.

I remember so well at first that I was determined not to *become* the deep sadness and trauma that I had experienced. I did not want to be that person who constantly refers to their lost loved one, years down the road, in every conversation. I wanted to move down the road independently. I did not know that, in truth, the loss of that person may always be my closest companion on the journey, and that this is something none of us can escape. While this "escape" may seem desirable, it is not healthy or realistic.

As Mary Oliver says in her poem "Love Sorrow," she (i.e. the loss or sorrow) is "mine now." I must "brush her hair, help her into her little coat, hold her hand," and most of all, "smile, that she does not forget the world before the lesson," and that she will begin to grow.

She has grown for me and for our family. As I reread this journal, I am in awe of our experience. I recognize the tumult and trauma. I cry for the innocence we lost. And, I know that it will all live within us always, while we all wear our (at first) ill-fitting coats that now have become closer to our individual sizes and tastes.

Emma, at twenty-nine, is living in Gardiner, Montana, with her partner, Mike. They both graduated with master's degrees in education in environmental science. She is now the director of Little Peoples Learning Center, an early-childhood-education program in Mammoth, Wyoming, just inside the gates of Yellowstone National Park. Her backyard is full of bison and the beautiful terraces of Mammoth Hot Springs. Mike is an environmental educator for the nonprofit Yellowstone Forever. In addition to working hard, they take full advantage of the extraordinary world in which they live, skiing and hiking in their time off. We all wonder, *Is it fanciful to imagine that perhaps Greg led Emma to this Grizzly-bear-loving young man from the Midwest?*

Lilly, at twenty-six, is living and working in Austin, Texas. After graduating from college, living and working full time in apparel design, her field of study in Seattle, she began to wonder,

Is this all there is? If so, I am not sure I want it! and saved her pennies to take off for six months of travel in South and Central America. This was a life-changing experience for Lilly, and one in which she felt the almost-tangible cheering on of her dad. Of many revelations she had while traveling, one was that a warmer climate and sun suits her soul. As a result, she moved to Austin, Texas, and is a designer for Sock Club while pursuing her love of pottery, paddle boarding, and her new puppy.

Clara graduated from St. Edwards University in Austin with a major in photography. Her passion has been ignited by alternative photo processing, which, coincidentally, Greg was just learning when he was ill. We recently had a celebratory family gathering for her senior photo show, which consisted of a project she displayed using Greg's old negatives over the years overlaid with hers. She has come back to the Northwest for the year and will take off in June to lead trips for Alpengirl, a teen summer-adventure camp for girls. She has left her sister and her college life in Austin with mixed emotions and a genetic sense of adventure.

For young women who lost their father way too early in life, I marvel at their tentative steps through the world while they learn to understand their loss and grief. It has been filled with bewilderment and revelation as they work to integrate the legacy of a father who loved them as deeply as any father could. I will never make light of the knowledge of how painful it was for him to leave them. I carry that precious jewel in a treasured chamber of my heart, and work hard to honor it. I will always wonder at the course of events that led me to be the one to live out these years as sole parent to these beautiful young women.

I spend most of my life wondering as I rebuild and reframe the future so different from the one I expected and signed up for. I have worked hard and accomplished much. I have created a wonderful life, and I live in the realization that, though it is not a life I chose, it is a life I love. The experience of love and loss has changed me for the better.

I imagine that from an outside perspective, I look resilient and perhaps even somewhat accomplished. I probably look like the strong, badass, independent widow I wanted to be. And yet, I have learned that the process of incorporating my old life with my new one is longer term than I ever wanted or imagined it would be. I am always becoming.

As I look out on this spring, green morning, I feel a bit like the crazy rhubarb plant that somehow grew out of the compost where I least expected it. I have left the rhubarb right where it is, because it signifies determination and an irrepressible battle against all odds. Today for me, life has more moments of joy than sorrow.

On our wedding invitations, we had a quote from Rilke: *Live the questions now. Perhaps then, someday, you will gradually, without noticing, live into the answer.*

I am grateful for the continued opportunity to love and live into the mysteries.

I remember when Greg was first diagnosed, and I was obsessed with the thought that there are people who die alone. How could this be? And, how is it that our family has so much of an abundance of love? That will be one of many mysteries that will fill me with wonder for the remainder of my days.

All I can say I know for sure is that we are all meant to walk with each other as we navigate the deep joys and sorrows which make up the mystery that we call our lives. I feel such gratitude for all who walk with me.

Nancy Ewert

When it's over, I want to say all my life
I was a bride married to amazement.
I was the bridegroom, taking the world into my
arms.

. . . I don't want to end up simply having visited
this world.

—Mary Oliver, "When Death Comes"

ACKNOWLEDGMENTS

I feel such deep gratitude for so many who supported and encouraged my writing along the way. "There is a book here. You must keep writing!" You know who you are, and so do I.

I thank my writing group, Kip, Marcia, and Diane, for bearing witness through laughter and tears. Thanks to Steve Horn for his professional photography expertise and consistent encouragement along the way. I thank the CaringBridge organization for providing the online, life-sustaining platform of communication for those facing serious illness. And deepest appreciation to Abe Louise Young, my writing coach, who held my hand and gently loved me through every page of the process of creating this book.

ABOUT THE AUTHOR

Photo taken by Clara Ewert

Nancy Ewert lives with her devoted black lab, Bella, on a five-acre homestead on a small island off the coast of Washington State. She is a writer, cook, quilter, and active participant in her small, vital community. Her greatest joys are her children, her deep friendships, her garden, and long walks absorbing the beauty of the natural world around her.

Visit www.livinganddyingwithoutamap.com to learn more.